44

Glenna Rachael Hamill

Two Great Asiatic Lovers

JAHANGIR and Nur Mahal belong to the company of the world's great lovers. Their legend lives with the histories of Antony and Cleopatra and Abélard and Héloïse, but it has not been recorded hitherto in modern English literature.

In his studies of Tamerlane and Genghis Khan, Harold Lamb became fascinated with the figure of Nur Mahal, the lovely desert-born Persian girl who became the uncrowned ruler of the Mogul Empire at the height of its glory. She was the first love of Prince Jahangir.

Banished by Akbar, the Emperor, she did not meet Jahangir again until he was a middle-aged despot brutalized with power, wine, drugs, and pleasure.

Fighting the enmity of the palace-born harem and the cabals of a court built upon intrigue, she kept the last sparks of life in Jahangir's debauched body while she ruled the empire for him. This is her history as only the author of *The Crusades* could have written it.

NUR MAHAL

NUR MAHAL

DRAWING BY E. PARIN D'AULAIRE

NUR MAHAL

BY
HAROLD LAMB

Garden City, N. Y.

DOUBLEDAY, DORAN
& Company, Inc.

MCMXXXV

AUTHOR'S NOTE

THE *story of* Light of the Palace *is told in this book. It is not history or biography, because the women who lived behind the veil can never find their way into the pages of scholars, except as names.*

This narrative is the truth, so far as one man's research can make it. Nur Mahal—Light of the Palace —played her part in the reigns of three of the great Moguls. The chief characters and the events of the narrative are also historical.

Yet it is the peculiarity of the beautiful Persian who ruled India from the side of a dissolute emperor three centuries ago that the events of her life are not so arresting as her personality.

This book, then, is an attempt to bring one woman from the silence that surrounded the lives of those who wore the veil.

ILLUSTRATIONS

NUR MAHAL

I

T WAS the year of our era 1605. The age, it seems, was one of exploration. Elizabeth of England had died a little while before, most unhappily, writhing on the floor in convulsions. Shakespeare was still writing, engaged at that time upon the manuscript of the play *Antony and Cleopatra*.

The great Spanish Empire had passed through its golden generation under Philip II, after the conquest of Mexico and Peru in the New World and the disaster of the Armada. Farther to the east the empire of the Tsars, isolated in its snowbound forests, had been ruled by the hand of the adventurer Boris Godunov, who was then upon his deathbed.

Venturesome fleets were making settlements along the coasts of the Americas. Two small sailing ships had made the voyage around the globe, bringing in,

after years of absence, a burden of loot and many
strange tales—proving to the last doubters in Christian Europe that the earth was indeed round, and
that it disclosed in the little-explored East more
wonders than philosophers had dreamed of.

Chief among these wonders was the empire of the
great Moguls.

Some of the voyagers called it India. It was so
vast compared to the lands of Europe that Portuguese priests who had penetrated farthest could
give only a rough idea of its extent—saying that it
overran the deserts of the Baluchis to the west, and
the hills of the Afghans, while to the north it
stretched as far into the heights of mid-Asia as men
cared to go. It included, here, the earthly paradise
of Kashmir, running southeast through the foothills
of the Himalayas, mountains sacred to the pagans,
snow-crowned. It crossed the delta of the Ganges, as
far as the jungle of Burma.

This northern region with its governing city of
Lahore was the heart of the Mogul dominion.

But it extended a thousand miles or so to the
south, past the reigning city of Agra and the hills
of the Rajputs, to the elder India—down to the tip
of the mighty peninsula.

So said the voyagers, adding that the Mogul empire was made up of a dozen different peoples,
speaking different languages and worshiping everything from the prophet Muhammad to gods of
wood and stone, immemorably old. A hundred millions of people, they said. And the wealth of Asia
flowed into the court of the great Mogul. Toward

this wealth the eyes of European traders were drawn.

India, however, remained indifferent to the affairs of Christendom. It knew the people of the West only as barbarian shipmasters, who landed cloth merchants and black-robed priests at the seaports. Hitherto these men from the sea had been shrewd and more or less understandable Portuguese. Now the first English were sailing in.

In the year 1605 Jahangir seated himself upon the throne—sitting upon the black stone that bore an odd reddish stain, left, he had been told, by blood shed in former years. It pleased Jahangir to be emperor at last. To rule would be a new pastime, and Jahangir had a passion for new toys. He could never manage to take life seriously.

Outwardly he was heavy and long of limb. His head had an indolent, tawny fairness, with keen dark eyes and the lined flesh of a voluptuary. He had not the least doubt of the majesty which invested his person. Was he not the Shadow of God upon Earth, Pillar of the Faith, King of Justice, Conqueror of the World?

He was absolute monarch, more remote from his people than the Cæsars from the Romans. His person was precious, his coming hailed as a good omen, his anger accepted as inevitable. In the mosques his name was breathed with that of Allah. He was the *Padishah*—the emperor—and who would dare reproach him for his vices, when his will was law?

Moreover, his ancestors had been conquerors. The

first great Mongol,[1] Genghis Khan, had subdued the larger half of Asia. Thereafter Tamerlane—known to the Moguls as Timur—had built an empire about Samarkand. A descendant of Tamerlane, Babar, had wandered from Samarkand through the hills into India and had become the first of the Mogul emperors of India.

Jahangir had read Babar's memoirs with appreciation. His great-grandfather had been an unusual soul, capable of running along the parapet of a castle wall carrying a man under each arm, and of drinking both wine and spirits for a night without apparent ill effect—a good judge of verse he had been, as well. All these qualities appealed to Jahangir.

In his grandfather Humayun he found less to admire, since Humayun had been occupied in holding together the skeleton of the new empire, besides devoting himself to opium instead of choice wines.

But his own father, Akbar, had been a truly remarkable man. A genius of extraordinary force, who had needed no more than three hours' sleep in the twenty-four to do the work of a half dozen minds. "In actions," Jahangir said of him, "he was not like men of this world."

Akbar had established the dominion upon a firm foundation, enlarging the boundaries and drawing up a code of laws for everything from elephant breeding to horticulture. Akbar had experimented himself with all that came to his notice, including

---

[1]Mogul is actually the word Mongol, softened by translation into a different speech.

tobacco and mysticism. He had even forsaken women in his last years, and had devised a religion of his own. He had retained the energy of his Mongol forbears, while acquiring the brilliance of the native Hindu intellect. In his generation the heat of India had not yet drained away the endurance of the barbarian conqueror.

Jahangir had inherited his father's physical strength and taste for stimulants, with the indolence of his Rajput mother. He was the first of the Mogul line to grow up within a palace, knowing nothing of hardships and little of war. From his birth he had been the acknowledged heir; when Akbar's prime minister expressed disapproval of him, Jahangir had the official assassinated. Once he dallied with a plot to poison his father but contented himself with rebelling. Akbar tricked his son into submission, slapped his face in private as condemnation for allowing himself to be tricked, and deprived him of opium for ten days to permit him to meditate upon his unfilial conduct. Akbar always cherished a stubborn affection for his wayward son.

When Akbar was in his tomb, Jahangir, ascending the throne, discovered with relief that his father had so ordered the government that he need devote little attention to it. Instead, he set himself to the agreeable task of tasting as emperor the pleasures of life. In this quest he was endowed with the physical energy of his forefathers and the discernment of an epicurean philosopher.

Almost his first act was to order the bell of justice —near the wall of the Agra citadel a post was to be driven at the river's edge, and a gilded chain to be hung from the post to a window of the palace. At the end of the chain near his sleeping chamber a cluster of gold bells would be suspended. Jahangir announced that any man with a grievance could tug at the outer chain and sound the bells in the Presence. No one apparently attempted to do so, but the conceit pleased Jahangir. He had, in reality, a nice sense of justice.

For six years after his accession he experimented with his hobbies, disturbed only by the brief revolt of his eldest son. Women and hunting seemed to divert him most, although he had a collector's craving for precious stones, particularly rubies, and a keen interest in verse-making. From the beginning of his reign he had written his memoirs with his own hand.

It was on the eve of the sixth New Year feast, on the twenty-first day of March in the year 1611, that he listened with appreciation to a letter of congratulation sent by his brother monarch Shah Abbas of Persia.

"May the King of Increasing Fortune, the World Gripper, Possessor of Power over the Planets—Lord of Happenings, exalted as Alexander, Index of the Book of Life, Perfect Mirror of the Glory of God . . ."

Jahangir thought that the Shah's writers had a nice taste in phrases. He was not vain—he accepted praise as a matter of course.

But through the long hours of that New Day, the first of spring, he tasted in imagination the pleasure that would come with the evening. Then the women would have a festival in the palace garden. And to this Jahangir would go not as India's emperor but as a man seeking amusement.

It was the hour of candle-lighting. A clear moon overhung the river. A breath of hot wind from the sandy plain swayed the curtained barriers about the garden on the river's bank.

Stalwart Afghan women slaves stood within the barriers, holding shields and scimitars indifferently while they stared at the booths hung with orange blossoms and hibiscus. Colored lanterns glimmered among the fruit trees. Girl slaves ran lightly over the carpets that covered the grass.

Ripples of laughter and the soft undertone of whispers passed from booth to booth. Wives and daughters of the nobles had gathered here unveiled to masquerade for a few hours as bazaar traders. Embroideries and jewels lay about them, and rank was forgotten while they seized the precious moment to gossip without fear of being overheard by their own attendants.

Music wailed from the dark mass of the palace, and the emperor's women began to wander through the garden, their eyes swift to notice the garments and bearing of the *amirs'* ladies, even while they pretended to bargain for purchases.

" 'Tis for a gift I seek this armlet, and I have so little money"—this from the lips of a woman who could have covered the carpet with gold pieces, if she had wished.

"And my price also is so very little. I paid forty rupees for it—see, the pearls are matched, and the silver hath gilt upon it"—so answered the keeper of the booth, whose silver palanquin rested by the outer courtyard.

"Am I witless, not to know the worth of such a thing? Verily, I will give thee twelve rupees."

"May Allah forbid! But since it is for a gift, I will make the price thirty and five."

"Then will I find a better in the shop of Ahmad the Bokharian under the broken arch—true pearls, at a lesser price."

Laughter greeted this, for neither of the high-born ladies had set foot in the Agra bazaar in their lives. But all the listeners had heard of the jewel merchant Ahmad.

"And thou wilt find his silver to be lead beside this. See the mark upon it, and now"—in a loud whisper—"will I make the price to thee thirty rupees."

"Lick thy palm!"

The barter between guest and palace woman ran on until a price of twenty and two was agreed on, when the seller scored a hit by demanding *bakhshish* to sweeten the sale, and testing every coin—although the buyer's servants had given her gold instead of silver.

To haggle to the last quarter coin and then to overpay, that was the spirit of the fair. When a slender Rajputni who traced her ancestors back for ten centuries lisped a bazaar epithet as to the morals of thieves, cries of "Good—good!" greeted her. A young Tartar, whose slant eyes told of the blood of Cathay, nibbled at sugared ginger with all the assurance that perfect teeth can give, while a Chagatai Turk who had once held the favor of a king made display of an ivory-white skin, unpowdered, as she swept from booth to booth, and even the dancing girls cast sidelong glances after her.

These courtesans of the outer world were present in the garden by Jahangir's favor. He had wished the Gilded Ones to share in the merriment of the palace-bred, or perhaps he had wished to disturb the noblewomen. No one could be quite certain what whim moved him, at times. But the dancing women dared not speak to the others. In silent groups, wearing all their splendor of bracelets and anklets and coiled pearls, they listened to the gay chatter, understanding just as well as their sisters the lilting Persian and the harsher Turkish, as well as their own Hindi. For they were skilled in many things.

Incense from the booths mingled with the scent of orange blossoms. By the edge of the pool a dancing girl moved deftly in perfect time to the whisper of a lute, her shape mirrored in the dark water below.

Jahangir had begun to enjoy himself. He had bargained with boyish zest, calling to the black eunuchs who followed him about to dip both hands in the money sacks. He glanced at the girl by the pool, and on a sudden impulse ordered all his attendants away. He was the only man in the garden, and it pleased him to go apart into the shadows to watch and listen unseen.

Not quite unseen, for the *luli* ended her dance,

and pretending to think that he had summoned her, walked carelessly by. Irritably he motioned her away and turned to go elsewhere.

A booth apart from the others, where embroideries had been spread in the glow of a single lantern, obstructed his path. Jahangir picked up the light, with an apology.

"Thy forgiveness, princess——"

The words ceased in a quickly drawn breath. Jahangir looked into the dark eyes of a woman clad in the white of mourning. And the eyes caught at his memory. They drew him back through the years, until he forgot the garden with its throngs. They became the frightened eyes of a young girl. In another garden in a red stone city, when he had been barely a man grown, still the prince, the son of Akbar.

This other garden also had a pool, hidden by dark cypresses from the latticed windows of the *zenana*. Lotus blossoms covered the water near one corner— Jahangir's memory after nineteen years held fast to the blossoms, and the first shadows of sunset when the heat of a glowing sky lessened and he searched idly through the zenana garden.

No women met him on the paths. They kept out of his way, at that time. When he had been a child the younger ones had teased him and fondled him, and laughed at his retorts—except in the rooms of the queen, his mother. Then, when men had taken his schooling in hand, outside the zenana, some of the foreign slave girls had found opportunities to caress

him, arousing his passions. One of these Akar had
ordered buried alive. Anarkali had been her name—
a sallow Hindu, indifferent to hazard. After that
the younger women did not risk seeking open
intimacy with him. Besides, at that time the prince
treated their advances with scorn. Was he not the
acknowledged heir, with a small army at his command and no one except his father to take precedence
of him?

As he walked he caught flowers from the shrubs,
pulling them apart and letting them fall to the
ground. When he came to the edge of the pool he
picked up pebbles and began to throw them at the
lotus blooms. Being gifted with a true eye and a
powerful arm, he was soon cutting the buds to pieces
and littering the surface of the water with the fragments of leaves.

"Stop it!"

The sharp command, vibrant with pent-up feeling, astonished him. In the deep shadow under the
cypresses a girl was sitting, her legs curled under
her, and when he strode over to her she turned her
head away but did not try to flee. Her slight figure
appeared to be poised, waiting. Curiously he stared
at the long hair that hid her throat. It was nearly
black, and evidently she had no veil.

"Turn," he bade her gruffly, "and look!"

Picking up a stone he drew back his arm, expect-
ing a sidelong glance or a cry of pretended fear.
Instead the girl faced him swiftly, her eyes dark
with anger. Her clear skin had no tinge of coloring

upon it. It seemed to be transparent, glowing from an inner light.

"I see Akbar's son behaving like an ox-herd. Look *thou!*"

She pointed at the water, whispering, "My blossoms." Jahangir lifted the stone for another throw and let it fall. He started to reprimand her imperiously for using *thou* to him, and to mock her for calling the emperor's garden her own.

"Are they thine?" he asked, instead.

Only a nod answered him. The heir of the Mogul considered her with real surprise. She did not rise, although he was standing; she made no effort to catch his eye; instead she seemed quite satisfied now that the havoc in the pool had ceased. When he sat down beside her and questioned her he learned that she was an outlander, daughter of a Persian who had sought service at the court. She was fourteen years of age, and her parents called her Mihri—Beloved.

"And the place of thy birth?" Jahangir demanded.

"The desert, near Kandahar."

This struck Jahangir as remarkable, if she were not mocking him. Such girls as this, of Mihri's beauty, were born in the women's quarters of the palaces. "But why—what brought thy mother into the desert?"

"A caravan. We were coming to India, because my father wished it. We had three camels but no money or goods."

Jahangir felt a growing curiosity. This girl seemed to be indifferent to what he thought—sitting chin on hand, watching the surface of the water from beneath lowered lashes.

"What happened then?" he asked. "And how did they care for thee?"

"The caravan went on," she responded indifferently, "and I went with it, then."

Strange, a girl appearing in the midst of men and beasts moving over barren land, with only a brief halt for such an event. Jahangir knew that priests had chanted in the temples of the land to ward off the Nine Perils at his birth, and princesses had prayed over his Rajput mother, to save her from the after-fire, while Akbar's hand had scattered gold through the streets of the red city. . . .

"Well, where is thy home now?"

A bewildering smile lighted the face beside him. "In our hills."

Jahangir could not understand. It appeared that Mihri's father had told her of the hills of Khorassan where they had once lived. And now Mihri thought of the hills she had never seen as her true home, because she did not like India. A moment ago she had been the most matter-of-fact of human beings; now she was playing with a fancy. . . . He suspected that the eyes under those long lashes studied him unseen. What an ivory pallor upon the slender throat against the mass of dark hair! Of what could she be thinking, so aware of him and still so remote? So impassive, and yet alert—when she stirred, so like a bird.

Yes, she did resemble a bird, perched beside him upon the earth at the edge of the water. Untouchable and untamed and only for the moment quiet. If he took her within his arms, it would be like holding a wild pigeon. If he touched her——

She *had* been watching him from the corners of her eyes. When he stretched out his hand she was on her feet, unsmiling.

"Your Loftiness, it is past sunset, and I must go into the mahal. Listen!"

The high-pitched cry from minarets announced the evening prayer. *Come to prayer . . . come to the house of praise . . . prayer is good. . . .*

Cunning crept into Jahangir's mind—he who made no pretense of prayer except in public. "Late it is," he said evenly, "and almost past the moment. We can still repeat the namaz with the last bowing. Here."

He slipped the sleeveless *khalat* from his shoulders, spreading it on the ground between them. While hastily he washed hands and feet in the pool, Mihri hesitated. Then impulsively she went through the motions of washing and knelt on the far edge of the cloak, facing the west, her clear voice whispering the sonorous Arabic phrases.

Beside her Jahangir repeated the evening prayer absently. Shadows quite covered the pool. Scent of sun-warmed roses still lingered, mingled with the scent of Mihri's hair and the faint fragrance of her body.

When she stood up her eyes were full and quiet. They looked beyond him, unaware of him, questing beyond the garden, expressionless. A strange anger stirred in his veins, and he felt the hot moisture of tears under his eyes. His fingers closed over her hand, and he heard her voice:

"What is it?"

His arm circled the slender shoulders, and he buried his face in the dark tangle of her hair. . . . So had wild pigeons struggled in his grasp, their wings beating softly, futilely—the frightened heart throbbing against him. But she drew the scarf of her sleeve over her face, and when she did so her bare arm lay white against the red of his khalat upon the ground.

When Jahangir released her, twilight had settled down, veiling the hot sky. The girl swayed upon her feet—turning blindly from the pool, stumbling against a cypress. Jahangir felt a pang of pity, that she had hurt herself. "Mihri!" he called, following her. But the white figure eluded him, passing beyond his sight.

He went back to the pool where his cloak lay. For a moment he stared down at the water. Why, it was covered with the fragments of flowers. He dipped his hands in the water, splashing it over his hot forehead. . . .

That night he slept badly, and assured himself that he had taken too much wine late in the evening. He thought often of Mihri's eyes, and wondered if they would stir him to compose a poem. After sunrise he went back to the zenana wing of his father's palace, meaning to find out the girl's position among the women. It would be a simple matter to take her into his own household.

So Jahangir thought. But he found—a boy

zenana-bred never forgets the secrets of the curtained rooms—that something had happened to close the avenues of discovery. Women attendants greeted him with covert glances and deftly avoided even the most innocent-seeming questions. If such a person as the Persian girl Mihri existed, they seemed blandly unaware of it. She had become elusive as a child of the djinn-folk, while Jahangir grew at first impatient and then angered and then deadly earnest in his quest for her. He felt that these women had banded together to take from him, the prince-heir of the empire, the one thing he desired most.

From Ruqaiya, a wife of Akbar, he learned eventually that Mihri had been thoughtless; that evening she had appeared sobbing among the elder women, who had taken her aside to an upper terrace and had talked with her. Now Akbar had heard the tale, and fear of the emperor's anger had sealed the tongues of the palace. Even Jahangir's insistence could not break that seal.

Months passed without a trace of the Persian girl, until whispers ran through the palace, and Jahangir heard what Akbar had commanded to be done with her. Mihri had been married to a young Persian, a soldier, and the couple had journeyed from the court, perhaps to the distant hills of Khorassan. No one knew, but Jahangir understood that he had lost the girl. With an ordinary marriage he might have dealt casually. With this marriage, under Akbar's explicit order, he could not meddle. He did learn the Persian's name—Ali Kuli—and nothing more.

It was characteristic of him, because she had been

denied him, that he did not cease to desire Mihri. Yet something more than his self-esteem had been hurt. The doormen of the zenana told the bath slaves, who whispered to the ladies' attendants, that the son of Akbar did not walk again in the corner of the garden by the blue lotus pool. But even they who watched by his couch of nights did not know how the girl's face tortured his memory as year passed after year with other women married to him and children born to them.

Until in the garden of Agra's citadel in this New Day feast nineteen years later, by the glow of the lantern in his hand, he looked into the eyes of Mihri again and recognized her upon the instant of those foolish words:

"Thy forgiveness, princess——"

The few men who saw the woman Mihri unveiled have left still fewer descriptions of her. Her name, it seems, was enough to set her apart from her sisters. One chronicler speaks casually of her dark blue eyes, while another is certain they were black. Even the portrait painters of the court do not agree.

Strict Moslems observe that she had the semblance of a statue into which life has come. But they were her antagonists—Muhammad proclaimed all statues evil. Suffice it that she impressed them as a woman isolated from others by some circumstance beyond their knowing. They were all, except one, eager to accuse her.

What Jahangir saw, then, in the booth during the garden *fête* of the New Day was the same slender

Mihri of their first meeting. But now a woman who had passed her thirtieth year. He saw the shadows under the eyes, and the soft curve of the cheek that melted into the slim throat.

"Put down the lantern, my lord."

Her voice had grown softer, more modulated. Only then was he aware that he had thrust the smoking cresset lamp close to her face, and that his hand was quivering, so that tiny flames leaped from the holes in the brass lamp.

"Mihri," he asked, "how came you here?"

She was smiling at him curiously. "Have I not been here, O Padishah, for years?"

"Thy—your garments." His words came clumsily. "For whom do you mourn?"

"For my husband, these four years, my lord."

"He died—how?"

Fleetingly the woman searched his eyes before she answered, "By the sword." And she lifted one of the embroideries lying between them. "Will the Padishah not deign to cast his eyes upon this piece? The thread is of gold."

The figures that had drawn nearer in the shadows had not escaped her notice and she knew that sharp ears were taking count of their words. The challenge to play roused Jahangir.

"Nay—" he could not think how to call her—"O mistress of the shop, that piece is bazaar goods. Now that one yonder is worn and torn at the edge, yet it hath good color, and it might please me."

Lifting a blue cloth in her fingers, Mihri studied it. "Surely this blue is of the evening sky, and the silver of the stars. Is it not written that the beauty of twilight never endures? So what matter a little wear or a few rents? What price will you pay?"

"Let the seller name the price!"

"After all, it is a poor piece—my hands made it. Now here is pearl-sewn cloth-of-gold, more fitting for an emperor."

Disappointed, Jahangir essayed a jest. "May an emperor wear nothing but gold cloth and pearls? What if he be an artist?"

But the woman was looking beyond him, bending her head in salutation to others approaching. With her attendants bearing lights, the dowager of the palace drew near, her withered figure wrapped in the same white as Mihri's. Salima Begam had been a favorite of Akbar, and she was one of the few who could influence Jahangir; even at seventy-five years she carried her head erect, and she could see surprisingly well. "*Ai—ai,* Shaikhu Baba—Old Daddy— you have found the fairest flower of the garden. Yet did I find her before you, so she serves to bring delight into my empty hours. What have you bought of her?"

Salima Begam, a princess of the Tamerlane line, still called Jahangir by his boyhood name, as Akbar had called him in the years when the court inhabited the red city. For nearly two generations she had dominated a restless multitude, and no one dared gainsay her. Placing a thin hand that quivered a little upon his sleeve, she complained:

"I have tasted no sweetmeats this evening. In the scarlet pavilion they await thy sitting down to the supper dishes, and, by Allah, I have no mind to go hungry through a festival."

As they made their way around the pool—Salima took pleasure in walking before other dowagers who could not manage such exertion—Jahangir whispered, "Is she truly in thy household, Perfection of Beauty?"

"Have I ever lied to thee, except at need, Shaikhu Baba? Aye, her father placed her with me, two years ago. Four years hath she been a widow like me—like to me. She reads Persian poetry nicely. I do not care for it, but I love her voice. What is it to thee?"

The faded eyes peered up at him, then wandered toward the lights.

"And she is not to have another husband? She cares for no one?"

The old princess adjusted her headcloth and sniffed faintly. "Does the wind blow here, or there? I do not know. Khoda mi-danad—only God knows. Besides, I am faint with hunger, and at such times I do not think very clearly."

"She came here tonight at thy wish, Perfection of Beauty."

"And why not, Shaikhu Baba? By Allah, Ruqaiya, who is younger than I, but tints her cheeks— Ruqaiya hath no lovelier handmaiden than Mihri. That reminds me, a maid of mine whispered me that thou asked of Mihri the manner of her lord's death. Bethink thee, before asking that again. Nay, do not look at me like that. The praise to God, we are here at last."

Probably only Salima in all India would have

dared go before Jahangir into the supper pavilion while the ladies of the court rose to make prostration. But her knees were trembling with the long walk, and she felt that she must settle down in her place before Ruqaiya's alert eye noticed her weakness.

Jahangir retired early from the festival. Bidding his attendants find and bring to him one of his cup companions, a young Persian poet, he entered the palace and passed through the nearly empty chambers of the *harem* to a secluded sleeping room opening upon a balcony—a place where he was accustomed to drink undisturbed. A cup had been made ready for him, spiced wine strengthened by a dash of spirits, and he sipped at this in silence until the poet appeared in the curtained entrance and ran forward at the emperor's nod to cast himself on the carpet, pressing his right hand to his forehead.

"Farrash," Jahangir observed, "thou knowest the household of thy countryman, Ghias ad Din, the minister of my treasury?"

"May the Heaven-born be content. I have sat often at the tablecloth of Ghias Beg, whose wisdom——"

"His wisdom I know. It is of his daughter Mihri I wish tidings. But first empty a cup with me." The Mogul struck his hands together softly, and a negro knelt beside the attentive poet, presenting to him a gold goblet filled with white spirits—and with more than a little opium added at Jahangir's instructions.

Farrash had come hastily into the Presence smelling
so strongly of musk that the emperor was convinced
he had been drinking. So another cup of double distilled spirits with opium should dull the quick wits
of the poet just enough to lead him to tell something
of the truth. And Jahangir wished very much to
know why Salima had warned him not to question
the manner of death that had befallen Mihri's husband. Quite well aware that she had come to the edge
of the grave, the old Tartar princess was not given to
idle words.

But he checked Farrash's flow of rhapsody with
an assurance that he was not in a mood for verses.
"I beheld the lady Mihri at the festival and she was
without companions. I alone came to her booth,
drawn thither by the lamp of her beauty."

Well he knew that this casual remark would act
upon the poet's eager mind like a torch upon laid
fuel. And Farrash had the gossip of the inner palace
at his tongue's end. Farrash would have heard long
since of the meeting years ago between the prince-
heir and the Persian girl in the mahal garden of the
red city.

"Verily," marveled the poet, "the Sun of Benevo-
lence was drawn to the lamp of beauty. Is it not
written in the Book-to-be-read: *'Verily ye shall taste
that which ye have stored up for yourselves'?* Yet
have I heard it said that the lady Mihri is like the
woman Zarka, who could see things far off, who is
like one sitting ever in a watchtower. She is solitary
as the evening star at the setting of the sun."

"What more is said of her?"

"The slaves of the mahal have whispered that she keeps not behind the curtain—that she goes forth into the world during the hours of darkness. Others say that she hath an evil spirit hidden in her, so that men who come under her eyes will be destroyed. And it is true, as the Padishah knoweth, that her husband——"

Farrash fell silent, his full lips parting in suspense.

" 'As I know!' But I know not. What befell him?"

"His fate, his just fate." After a glance at his master's face, the poet sobered visibly and chose his words with care. "Has the Padishah forgotten how, four years ago in the subah of Bengal there was the fire of unrest, and the smoke of conspiracy against the Shadow of God, and how you gave command to bring into the Presence certain of the unruly ones who were sowing the seeds of rebellion with the hand of lawlessness? By your command the governor, Kutb ud-Din, sought those unruly ones until a warrior among them called the Tiger Thrower——"

"I know that. It is written in my memoirs, for Kutb ud-Din was my foster brother, raised on the same milk that nourished me. By Allah, he was dear to me! He went with some men to fetch this Tiger Thrower, who was a rebel and a man of daring. The Tiger Thrower suspected that they had come to put an end to his life. He ran Kutb ud-Din through the bowels with his sword and was cut to pieces as he deserved, at the spot."

"True." Farrash lowered his voice. "The Tiger Thrower was Mihri's lord."

"How? Her husband was Ali Kuli—they had gone to the hills."

"And returned, O my Padishah. Ali Kuli was his name, until during a tiger hunt by an act of bravery he received the name Tiger Thrower."

"So the Persian died thus, by the sword?"

Jahangir meditated upon the curious working of fate—that Mihri's husband and his own foster brother should have put each other to death, as it were, in this fashion. Except for the loss of Kutb ud-Din he might never have known of it. There were thousands of rebels in the provinces in a year, and hundreds of such cases were brought before the Mogul.

Then a sudden thought pricked him. Salima's warning—Farrash's uneasiness! He, Jahangir, had given the order to arrest the Tiger Thrower, to bring him to court for judgment. True, the Tiger Thrower had perished in a sudden quarrel; yet he had suspected treachery, and everyone must suspect that the Mogul, upon coming to the throne, had planned the death of Mihri's husband. And he, unwitting, had written it down in his memoirs for all the court to see, as if in self-justification!

He became aware that Farrash was watching him with veiled eagerness. What a tale the rhapsodist would pour into curious ears! "Thou hast leave to go," he ordered curtly. "Stay—" forgetting his determination not to reveal his feeling—"hath—did this Tiger Thrower leave no children?"

"Only one, my Padishah, a girl, it is said."

"Her age?" He asked it helplessly, involuntarily.

"Thy servant hath seen the child." Farrash lowered his eyes. "She might be ten years."

"And who are the other wives of this—Tiger Thrower?"

"Such as he cannot afford a household. And who, having Mihri, would wish others? Nay, he had but the one."

Farrash had lost his poetic imagery in plain words, realizing that the powerful man before him was gripped by emotion.

"Go now," muttered Jahangir, "but never forget that thou hast spoken this night under the seal of confidence, which being broken, will bring thee to a slow death."

"Thy slave hath heard!" The poet flung himself upon the carpet. He had been present when Jahangir, upon his accession, ordered two hundred rebels to be set on stakes to wriggle out their lives and had led his son Khusrau down the avenue of the stakes, to impress upon the mind of the prince the fate of traitors. "Kulluk! I am thy minion, thy shadow——"

"Tell them at the curtain to bring more wine and admit no one."

When the poet had salaamed himself out, Jahangir divided his attention between the fresh cup and a sheet of paper upon which he scrawled idly. He felt that he could not write a good verse, to suit this new mood. He saw himself sitting in the *jharoka* window, looking out upon multitudes, himself alone. Always he had these throngs about him, pressing upon his attention, hiding events from him. No doubt they were all individual men, with homes and lives of their own; but he knew nothing of them except their insistence, to gain his mercy, to attract his attention. Beyond that, secrecy. Were they not really his enemies?

Farrash would not keep silent, but he, the Mogul, would never hear an echo of what the poet whispered. . . . Mihri's father, gray-haired, the very model of discreet courtesy—what did he know of *his* thoughts? They met nearly every day—Ghias Beg was the invaluable administrator of the empire's finances . . . Jahangir knew he took bribes.

They were all outside the window, gazing in upon him. Jahangir's hand moved the pen upon the paper. *"Ye shall taste that which ye have stored up for yourselves."*

That was sure. He emptied the cup, glanced at the red fire hidden within its rubies upon the base . . . fine jewels always caught his fancy. He tried to doze, and found the dark eyes of the Persian girl before him. She was in his arms, by the pool of the mahal in the red city.

She had lived in his imagination for years. Why did she not belong to him? He wondered what Salima had planned . . . Salima loved Shaikhu Baba, but she concealed some things from him.

And then the thronging images vanished from the Mogul's mind, leaving only the eyes of the Persian in a cool darkness. He felt comforted.

When the spring festival had ended, Jahangir asked Mihri in marriage, from her father, Ghias Beg.

The request of the Mogul, of course, amounted to a command. And the politic minister of the treasury had never opposed even a whim of his master. The marriage would unite his blood with that of the emperor, opening new fields to his ambition. Only Mihri's refusal could prevent it, and vehemently he urged upon her the folly of objection.

"Believest thou, O my father," she asked, "that the happenings of our lives are written—and that what is written will come to pass?"

"Yea, surely, Mihri." Inwardly Ghias Beg doubted it, but this was not a time to express doubt. "No greater honor could come to our house than that the Padishah, our lord, should take thee under his protection."

"And it is thy wish?"

"It is thy happiness and safeguard. And since I held thee in my arms by the caravan, I have wished that. Thou art the jewel of my life."

His thin hand touched her dark hair, and she smiled up at him. "Say to our lord that I, his servant, will enter his house."

Ghias Beg drew a long breath of satisfaction, assuring himself that Mihri would not have consented unless she had desired it. Until the day of the marriage he busied himself preparing gifts to offer Jahangir—knowing to a nicety his master's fondness for rubies of Badakshan cutting, hunting dogs and rare enamel work, with new guns chased with gold by the artisans of Persia. That day he gave a feast, opening his Agra house to all who claimed his protection, and casting silver to the throngs in the courtyard, so that they should know how he rejoiced at the honor of kinship with the Padishah. He himself went with all ceremony to the mosque, while Mihri, in her white widow's robe without ornaments, and Jahangir in jeweled *pagri* and state khalat stood before the judges and witnesses, to say—the Moslem marriage rite was no more than that—they would become husband and wife.

There was no court ceremony or banquet. When the *kadis* and the witnesses had departed, Jahangir led the Persian to a closed palanquin guarded by palace slaves, and escorted her to the citadel. In the grand court he dismounted, to walk by the palanquin —observed by a thousand eyes from the screened balconies. When she stepped from the litter, he led her by the hand through the Queen's Hall, to the curtain at the far end, where the eunuchs on guard prostrated themselves, and slaves hastened to draw back the embroidered curtain.

At the side of her husband the new wife entered the first corridor of the harem, and the curtain fell behind her. Within the door of the apartment he had allotted to her—where her own maids in festival dress awaited them—he closed the screen behind him with his own hand.

"This is thy house, O heart of mine," he whispered, and his hand sought clumsily to draw aside her veil. Her deft fingers went to his aid, to free the silk mesh from the headband, and when his eyes beheld the flower-like face flush swiftly under his gaze, he laughed softly. "Now, at last, there is nought between us."

But through the corridors of the harem whispers passed, wondering, questioning, prophesying: *The Persian girl had caught Jahangir again in the net of her charm. . . . He had broken precedent, taking a woman who had belonged to another, who had a child by that other . . . would he escape the fate of the Tiger Thrower . . . or would he soon tire of this stranger who was not palace bred?*

Early the next morning, Jahangir, who had retired to his own sleeping chamber, roused and asked the time of the couch servant who knelt at his feet. Hearing that dawn would come within a *ghari,* Jahangir summoned his bath slaves, and rose to plunge into the warmed and scented water that filled the deep tank of purple porphyry. When he had been dressed, he went to the wing of the harem he had given to Mihri. When the slaves in her anteroom hastened to press their foreheads to the floor, with a murmured "Hazrat-salamet—health to Your Majesty," he motioned to them to be silent.

"She sleeps?"

He made his way quietly to the roof terrace, conscious of the scent of crushed rose leaves. A colored lamp glowed on the floor, revealing the delicate fretwork of carved stone that screened Mihri's sleeping place. He could see her lying on a silk coverlet among heaped pillows, a white silk cloth covering her waist and breast.

Jahangir was a heavy man, yet he moved without a sound to the cushions beside her. His lined face softened as he watched her breathing slowly, until the red glow of the lamp dwindled as the first light crept through the lacework of marble. The curve of her cheek outlined itself against the heavy mass of her hair.

She was the same Mihri—was she looking up at him now through the shadow of the long lashes? And she belonged to him now. At the garden festival she had been a smiling statue, her eyes hidden behind the veil that some women knew so well how to draw about them. Now she had become alive, intimate, and lovely. And now she belonged to him—unknowable and untamable, and yet his.

A wailing cry sounded in the distance.

"Come to prayer, come to prayer . . . come to the house of praise."

It was the muezzin calling the dawn prayer, and Jahangir caught his breath at the swift memory of the garden in the red city. Mihri opened her eyes and smiled up at him. "Thou art here, my lord?"

"Aye," Jahangir blundered—"here."

Drawing the white silk about her, she shook back the tangle of dark hair upon her shoulders and knelt beside him, repeating the words of the muezzin quietly.

There was a strange hunger in his face when he bent over her at the end. "Beloved among women, art thou grieved by this marriage to me—wilt thou, rather, be free?"

But Mihri's eyes lighted, and she smiled. "Heart of my heart, am I not thine?"

"Nay, thou art the Mogul's, to keep or to set free as he wills."

It was a boy's stubborn wilfulness, and Mihri laughed softly. "As he wills! Is the Heaven-born tired in the morning of the night's love? Verily that would shame me."

Seizing her head in his heavy hands, Jahangir shook it gently from side to side, laughing low-voiced. "Tired? Verily I was weary of life until the last evening. Never will we talk of separation again."

"Then," Mihri swayed her body in a half-mocking salaam, "is this, thy slave content. Now my lord is hungered, and in a little he must go to the jharoka."

At her summons the women brought trays and dishes, and Jahangir ate with keen appetite, while he wondered at this bride who could think of the morning's duty before the morning's meal. Suddenly the sun came up, flooding the river, the sandy plain and the palace wall with hot light. The marble fretwork cast a pattern upon them, and Jahangir wondered anew that it could increase Mihri's loveliness. He had been thinking pleasantly enough.

"I have a name for thee," he proclaimed, "a fitting name for the wife of the Padishah. Nur Mahal thou shalt be."

"Light of the Palace. A gracious name."

"It must be thine. Mihri thou art no more, Nur Mahal."

Reluctantly he rose, when the plain below the outer wall had filled with crowds awaiting his first appearance at the public window called the jharoka. It was nearly an hour after sunrise, and the people of

Agra came as usual to have a glimpse of their master.

"Let them wait," Jahangir said indolently. "Are they not always there? I shall order coins to be cast from the window, and we can watch."

Having announced his pleasure, he expected to hear no more of it; but the woman he had just christened Nur Mahal kept silence until he turned to her.

"How cool the air feels," she murmured, "in the shadow of this terrace, the gift of my lord. When the sun is low and the heat grows, after my lord hath come from his audiences, I will make all ready for him as it should be, scented with the rose scent——"

"What is that? I have known nothing like it."

"Attar of rose, my mother called it." Nur Mahal offered him a tiny silver flask, explaining how it was prepared from rose leaves boiled many times. With his quick interest in such details, he followed her words carefully, sniffing at the flask. "Take it with thee, my lord, lest thou forget—Nur Mahal—and return swiftly to thy servant."

Jahangir found that he was moving slowly toward the entrance, at her side, but he did not realize that he did so at her will.

"I have thought of a verse," he announced. "A poor offering to the flower of thy beauty, but still— '*I was mad with longing to meet with thee, and mad with grieving, to part from thee.*' Does it please thee a little, O heart of my heart?"

He composed, he knew, indifferently well, yet he had a nice appreciation of the best poetry: Farrash and the court versifiers would have gone into rhymed ecstasies at this effort, and he waited expectantly for the praise of his new love.

"Verily the delight of it will serve to ease the hours of waiting," she smiled up at him shyly, "until the coming of my lord."

As he made his way through the corridors to the waiting attendants, he thought how well Mihri— Nur Mahal she was—understood his moods, and how generous she was, to surrender him to the throngs waiting for him to dispense justice. The Hindu girl, Prithvi, would have laughed softly, triumphantly, if he had hinted that he would forsake the audiences to remain with her. He reflected that Prithvi used a heavy perfume of musk and aloes.

While he watched the parade of elephants across the plain by the river and a drill of the noble-born *ahadi* cavalry, he grew more content. Perhaps, since Nur Mahal had not praised the verse, certain words might be changed to advantage. He would not ask Farrash, but he would polish it secretly, himself . . .

The day of the Mogul was full indeed. From the jharoka he passed to the canopied court of public audience, where innumerable petitions were handed in from officer to officer, and a stream of newly appointed dignitaries appeared before him to make the salaam of gratitude and present their first offering to the feet of their lord. Jahangir looked over all the gifts with an attentive eye and picked out some curios to examine while the writers of the treasury made lists of the valuables. The people of his court understood well that the Mogul's fancy might be caught by some rarity, especially by rubies, for which he had a passion. Only when appeal was made to his personal sense of justice did he become serious.

At mid-morning he appeared in the private audience where the lords of India—Mongol, Rajput, and Afghan in state robes—pressed inside the silver railing, and under the ceaseless murmur of flattery a silent struggle for precedence went on about the black marble stone that formed the pedestal of the throne. Near the center of the stone Jahangir had noticed a reddish stain. It could not be cleaned away —he thought it might be iron in the rock—and he had been told that it was an old stain of blood, left there since the day when Tamerlane had laid in Samarkand the foundation of the Mogul empire. Jahangir, when he became weary, often stared at the stone. But today he occupied himself with the silver flask until Abu'l Hasan the portrait painter ventured to ask him the nature of the delicate new perfume that scented the air under the swinging peacock fans in the hands of the slaves.

" 'Tis attar of rose," Jahangir explained, pleased. "Let it be called—" he could not mention a woman's name in public—"atr Jahangiri."

Not until an hour after sunset, when he rose from the secret conference of the princes and amirs in the tower called the Shah's—the tower guarded by a chosen company of Turks, wherein not even a prince of the blood could enter without his written pass and no servants were allowed—was the Mogul free to retire through the Queen's Hall into the harem. He

did not wait to listen to the music the slave women
had prepared in the garden, but went to Nur
Mahal's chambers.

"Read thou to me," he said, "for I have no skill
at making verses, and in the Shah's tower—read
something to ease my mind."

She nestled against the cushions by his feet, half
smiling, without book or manuscript in her hand.
*"'Of nights the souls of men from out their cages
flee . . . Of nights the slave and sultan heed not
their misery. . . .'"*

Her low voice soothed him, and he noticed that
she repeated from memory without faltering. When
she had done he clapped his hands and chuckled.

"An enchantress of the night thou art! And lo,
here is the sultan who hath become thy slave." He
drew her supple body across his knees and bent to
look into the eyes upturned to his. "Thy slave."

It became apparent to those who heeded events
behind the women's curtain of the palace that Jahangir would not tire of his new love at once. He had
found something more than a plaything to divert
him.

II

IN THE red stone palace of Agra the harem of the Mogul formed a world apart. It began at the guarded curtain of the Queen's Hall, and extended through corridors and tiled chambers, out upon screened roofs and canopied courtyards, to the secluded garden with the pool. It emerged, behind hangings of tissue-thin silk, to a portion of the private council hall, where behind the partition of stone lacework the women could listen to the talk about the Throne. By scratching holes in the silk they could see the faces of the men.

This inner world of the women had many diversions—since the harem was also Jahangir's quarters for the night, and the nursery of his younger sons. It had its own baths and musicians. Bengali eunuchs came and went between it and the outer world, to make purchases for the women, but oftener to bring news to them.

36

The harem, or zenana, obeyed one master, Jahangir. But it was dominated by the eldest widow of Akbar. Salima, and her rival Ruqaiya, headed the Tartar branch of the family, and they were accustomed to obedience. In their youth they had journeyed with armies and had known the hardships of flights over mountain ranges, and thirst. Salima, it was said, once played polo and made arrows for the bows of her men. She had been known to sound the great kettledrums, to the horror of the armed guard, who dared not interfere with the veiled Tartar woman. Nor did Salima take the veil very seriously.

A self-contained Rajputni, Jahangir's mother, was head of the Hindu women, who had become increasingly numerous. With the pride of an ancestry that traced back to the beginning of India, the Rajput ladies kept themselves from physical contact with the Moslem women, while many of them ate their hearts out with loneliness in this barbaric court of conquerors. They eased the long hours secretly with opium, and remained for the most part indifferent to the fortunes of the Moguls except where their own honor was involved.

Giving obedience to the elders, but secretly allied to their kinsmen of the outer world, Jahangir's dozen wives formed separate households within the harem. They were daughters of rajas or amirs, married from policy, and those who had no children became little more than names in the court. They cherished the hidden antagonism of the childless for the mothers of sons.

Less than the wives, but no less influential in the

harem world, were the *parastarha,* the favored concubines, with Prithvi at their head—Prithvi who
had once been a dancing girl, who wore the jewels
of a king's ransom upon ankles and arms. Her tame
leopard prowled the corridors, and, although its
claws had been drawn, the slave girls dreaded it.

The slaves formed a veritable legion. There were
the captives of wars from other lands, and young
girls inquisitive as foxes and avid for excitement.
There were the serving women and the trained
dancers and the blacks from Abyssinia.

The inmates of the harem were not cut off from
the outer world; their kinswomen could visit them
upon occasion, and the fathers of the noble-born
wives could enter the general halls. When the court
moved from Agra, some of them traveled with it.
But Moslem and Hindu alike were subject to the
law of *pardah*—they wore the veil and must remain
within the veil. They could not set foot alone beyond
the outer curtain, nor could they be seen by men
within it. They were as much captives as the gorgeous birds in the garden cages.

So, at least, they appeared to the multitudes when
the harem made a journey. The *mahalha-ye-shahi*—
the imperial ladies—emerged from the gates in
screened palanquins or camel litters or closed *how-
dahs* upon the elephants, surrounded by the harem
guards with cavalry in attendance and staff-men to
open a way before them. No man of the outer world
could approach within stone's throw, and it was the
part of wisdom to make prostration or turn away
when the Mogul's women passed.

In this aspect they were a part of the magnificent spectacle of the court; but within their own quarters they had another aspect still. The preparation of banquets and festivals was in the hands of some of the leading ladies. The best of them became dispensers of charity, aid to the thousands of Hindu and Moslem women, girls, orphans, child-widows, homeless, divorced, or beggared—the never dwindling multitude that has always suffered unheard behind the veil.

The halls of the royal ladies were never empty of those who came to beg money for a pilgrimage, cloth for children's garments, physic for the sick, judgment upon an enemy, or a spell to ward off a curse. Although the cry of the streets, "Need waits at the door," never sounded in these halls, the appeal of the women from outside never ceased.

The ladies were also clothiers and drapers extraordinary to the vast court. Their slaves and attendants worked at new fabrics, delicate embroidery, and the elaborate hangings that served at once for decoration and screening in the rooms of the palace. Slippers, girdles, jackets and robes-of-honor, turban cloth, bath wrappers, rug covers, and cushion cases, face veils, and a hundred other necessities were all the work of women's hands. Moving as it did through the heat of India, and maintaining display that amounted to continuous pageantry—having little use for massive furniture or metal utensils—the court of the Mogul demanded unending quantities of the finest fabrics. Even the elephants and horses had their elaborate trappings, and the traveling court lived in pavilions.

A new sheer silk from Cathay, or a finer cloth-of-gold
from Isfahan, a fresh purple velvet from the Portuguese merchants—these were important events to the
women. A clever design in embroidery brought its
imitators within a week, and a deft change in the
hang of a *sari* would be copied before sunset.

Some women had undergarments of silk so delicate
that they were cast away after a day's wear.

Of their many aspects the women of the harem
could present only one to Jahangir. They must appear to be the devoted servants of a never-sufficiently-
to-be-praised master.

When not in his presence—and few except the fa-
vorites or the elder ladies of his family saw him often
—they were part of the ceaseless struggle of the
harem. The fortune of their lives and the fate of
their relatives depended upon the amount of favor
they could win, if not from the head of all favors,
from those who shared his confidence and could make
claim upon his generosity. Power descended in im-
perceptible gradations from the gorgeous Prithvi or
the reverenced Salima to the most abject errand
runner of the most ill-favored and ignored concubine.

Favor brought them more than wealth in jewels
and slaves. It bestowed lands and the rents of towns
upon the more fortunate. But it gave a favored
woman no respite in the struggle. Dependents appeared to share in her power; if she had children,
they became rivals of other children born within the
harem. She was caught in a network of cliques, spy-
ing and spied upon. She must keep her ear continu-

ally close to the whispers of the corridors, and she must watch events in the outer world. She had become the head of a court of her own, and a moment's forgetfulness might lose her crown. From her rivals she could expect no mercy.

There were at that time two steadying forces in the Mogul's harem. The elder Tartar ladies exerted a certain almost masculine authority, but few of them survived, and they were old. And, except for the first years of Jahangir's reign, when his eldest son, Khusrau, had rebelled—the Rajput mother of that son committed suicide—the harem had not been divided as yet by civil war in India.

Nur Mahal entered the life of the harem in silence. Being a Persian, she found no countrywomen among the other wives; being the daughter of a wanderer from Khorassan, she had neither allies nor foes among the great Hindu and Moslem families of the court. She kept to herself, wearing always the white of mourning. They spoke of her as the ornament of the bridal chamber.

Her first meeting with the gorgeous Prithvi provoked a stir of interest. The Hindu dancer, going with her attendants to the bath, met the Persian alone in the flower court, and a hundred eyes fastened upon them eagerly—upon those two slight, almost childlike figures. Their glances clashed for a second.

With the swaying grace of a slave girl, Prithvi bent, throwing up her hand in the salutation of the dancer, the sunlight reflected from the tiles of the flooring flashing upon gold armlets and green silk. It

was inimitable, with just sufficient touch of mockery
to hint that it pleased her to do what Nur Mahal
could not do.

"Well done." The Persian's clear voice greeted
her instantly. "Verily thou knowest thine art, O my
sister."

And she was gone, moving as lightly as the dancer,
leaving a scent of rose leaves in the court. It was
Prithvi who looked after her thoughtfully, who
changed her mind about going to the bath and who
called for a mirror in the safety of her own chambers.
It seemed to her that her cheeks had grown too
chubby and that her eyes bulged a little. Whereupon
she fell into a fit of black brooding that even the flattery of her women could not ease.

Prithvi took pains thereafter to keep herself informed of all that took place in Nur Mahal's apartment. Bits of information drifted in to her. Nur
Mahal embroidered with her women—she made the
design for the new carpet cover herself—she touched
up her eyebrows in some way, but not with *kohl*—she
had no visitor except the emperor, who sent her a
new gift every morning—she had twice as many
slaves as at first—she sang to herself in Persian, sitting by the window, and she made faces at herself in
the mirror.

Nothing in all this to reassure the Hindu dancer,
who began to grow sullen, perceiving instinctively a
rival in the new wife. Tentatively she tossed a morsel
of gossip into the corridors. It was whispered that
Nur Mahal had come to court and had appeared
to Jahangir at the New Day feast to revenge herself

on the emperor for the death of her husband. It was explained that she knew the secrets of poisons, and had killed mice by the scent of attar of rose mixed with datura juice.

Salima heard and pondered, and paid a formal visit to Nur Mahal's rooms. She sent a woman to announce her coming and entered at the head of her ladies, wearing all her barbaric jewelry, with her face painted. Upon her lay the invisible robe of age and authority.

After a glance at the lined face, usually so benevolent, Nur Mahal greeted her with the half prostration of ceremony. For an hour hardly a word passed between them, while the Persian served the dowager with perfect jellies and savories, and sugared rice stained yellow with saffron. Finally Salima whispered to herself, opening and shutting her fan with a clash—she carried on such occasions one of the heavy fans of Cathay. The serving women left them alone.

"I am old," Salima vouchsafed, surprisingly. "After breath has passed from me, Ruqaiya will be head of the curtained rooms." And she peered at her companion.

But the Persian's face expressed nothing more than compassion and interest. The dowager had fallen into introspection, and the wife had drawn a veil over her feelings.

"Mihri," Salima cried, using the childhood name, "I took thee under the skirt of my protection when thou wert a widow. I arranged that the Padishah should see thee at the New Day."

Nur Mahal murmured her gratitude, but Salima was not satisfied.

"The Padishah's wives were shadows—except perhaps for the mother of Kurram. Wallahi, in my time it was otherwise. Did we not ride with his late Majesty from camp to camp, to share his counsels and serve his will at any hour? Who journeys now with the Padishah thy husband—except at times Prithvi the dancer?"

The Persian made no response, and the dowager snapped her fan with irritation. "Where is thy child? I do not see her here."

"Nay, it is not the place for one born outside the palace. Better that she should be as she is, with friends of her childhood."

"Not the place!" The Tartar's black eyes flashed angrily. "Is it not thy house, and—and——" She became silent. *"Ai-a,* it may be true. But what a thing to say, to me! Harken, thou wild panther, I grow old, and these fair young girls of the bridal rooms whisper behind my head. Like foxes they are, running this way and that into their burrows. Yet I hear, a little. Some of them give thy lord opium, overmuch of it, during the hours he is with them. . . . Opium! It was the stay and consolation of his grandfather. His two brothers Murad and Daniyal died of overmuch wine. . . . Daniyal ever loved hunting and horses—ay, he had one gun that he called Guide to the Grave. It was a large gun. Who can know his fate? When wine and spirits were forbidden Daniyal, by my lord, he begged of the musqueteers who guarded him that they bring in to him some double

spirits in the barrel of Guide to the Grave. They did
so, in that barrel which had long been nourished on
powder and rust, and when Daniyal drank from it,
he fell down at once. *Ai-a,* very soon he went to the
mercy of Allah, by reason of this same Guide to the
Grave. . . . And thy lord is like to him. I have
talked enough, and heard very little from thee."

Salima went off to her own reflections. A few days
later she pricked up her ears when word reached her
that Kurram had come to the mahal to offer a gift
to that panther, as the old Tartar chose to call Nur
Mahal.

It interested her vastly, because Kurram, taciturn,
emotionless, and supremely intelligent, was the favorite son of the emperor, a youth old enough to be
married. Kurram, the third son, born of a Rajput
mother was the very opposite of Jahangir, who had
once urged him to "Drink a little wine and be more
human." Although he would be heir to the empire,
and although he was Ruqaiya Begam's favorite,
Kurram went his own way, his eyes cold in a pallid
face. Salima wondered why he had come to offer a
present to Nur Mahal, and she wondered more when
she discovered that it was a horse.

Curiosity getting the better of her, she demanded
to be escorted down to the stone lattice of the open
gallery overlooking the outer court, where the elephants appeared upon occasion to take the women of
the harem upon a journey.

Already Nur Mahal was in the courtyard, stroking the mane of the slender gray Arab that Kurram
had selected for her. Salima heard her admiring the

red leather work upon the saddle and the jewels that weighted the rein. The Persian was veiled, wearing silk trousers and a white velvet vest. She really seemed to admire the horse.

"He hath easy paces," Kurram was saying to her. "Will you ride him, Nur Mahal?"

"Certainly—" the Persian's clear voice echoed within the gallery—"and now."

With no one aiding, she put her foot into the stirrup and was in the saddle, sitting astride, as all women did.

"Take care," Kurram warned her quickly. "He knows you not."

"Indeed he does."

Tightening the rein, she walked the gray Arab in a circle, then put him into a canter. At her touch he stopped dead, his head upflung—only to dart off with effortless ease at the pressure of her knees. Woman and horse moved in unison, wheeling at the corners, starting and stopping without visible sign. Her hair came unbound, tossing upon her slender shoulders. A fair picture, in the hot sunlight, that brought the slaves staring into the doorways.

Women from the harem joined Salima in the screened gallery, whispering shrilly at the unwonted sight of a wife of the Padishah exercising a horse in the courtyard.

"Shabash!" A voice rose above the others, to cry, "Well done!" But the cry was mockery, and Salima thought it came from one of Prithvi's maids.

"Yah bint!" another answered. "O girl!"

Nur Mahal could hear them without doubt. Making a final circuit of the ground, she reined in suddenly beneath the gallery. When Kurram ran forward to hold her stirrup, she slipped to earth on the side away from him, before he could touch her. Then with a swift flash of arms in the sunlight, she bound up her hair and stretched luxuriously. Throwing back her head she laughed up at the lattice—a ripple of sheer delight.

Salima frowned, but something within her stirred at the sight. Sitting with Ruqaiya that evening to discuss the incident of the horse she observed thoughtfully, "A panther will always be a panther, even if it be brought up among men."

"But if it be caged?"

"It will be as it was. Nur Mahal is desert born."

"I fear me, ay, I fear me. She hath laid her witchery upon Kurram."

"Upon Kurram!" Salima clashed her fan twice. "Is it her fault that he runs to hold her stirrup and casts sheep's eyes at her?"

Still, she worried herself into ill-temper at the strange alteration in the moody prince. He sent daily gifts to Nur Mahal, sometimes fruit and sometimes jewelry—Kurram had a passion for fine stones. Often he talked with her, discreetly enough, the two of them sitting in the Queen's Hall. Outwardly he seemed emotionless as ever, yet his glance searched among the women, if Nur Mahal were absent when he visited the outer rooms of the harem.

Not even the shrewdest eyes searching for scandal could find anything tangible in this. Kurram did not possess his father's fondness for hunting, or sporting

spectacles, even elephant fighting. At need he could
give excellent advice in the discussion within the
Shah's tower, or could take command of an army in
the field; but he lacked the inclination to play. What
he did was seriously done and well done. He had been
a frequent visitor to the harem in the past; now he
seemed to devote his attention to Nur Mahal.

"He wanders ever," Ruqaiya complained, "as if
searching for sorrow."

Kurram, as usual, said nothing at all. After a time
Nur Mahal permitted him to come into her own
rooms—as Jahangir's son he had that right. He saw
her there with other women. And among them he
noticed a young girl, Arjamand.

She sat apart, of course, at the embroidery stand
or among the maids on the cushions by the wall.
From head to foot she was swathed in muslin, with
only two mild brown eyes visible above the hint of
a pointed nose, but he distinguished her laugh from
the others, and he was grateful that Nur Mahal always had Arjamand by her. Why not, when the girl
was the daughter of her brother? He remembered
Arjamand as a child, stuffing herself with candy, but
she did not eat anything now in his presence.

"A dove," Ruqaiya said of her. Arjamand ate
sweets enough when no men were about.

To the spies of the harem, it seemed that Nur
Mahal kept the girl by her intentionally during
Kurram's visits. After all, Arjamand was of her
blood.

Inevitably the day came when the whisper went
through the corridors, *The prince hath a passion for*

*the ornament of the bridal chamber; he goes in
Jahangir's absence to sit at her feet, and she permits
—what?*

It was brought to the old Tartar ladies, who heard
it in silence. Nur Mahal was a stranger, a desert-
born, and she must look to herself. They waited for
a sign from Kurram, who went about impenetrable
as ever, until the evening when he bent his head before Ruqaiya and said:

"O first of Akbar's wives, will you speak to my
father, praying him to give consent that I take the
girl Arjamand[1] as my wife?"

Salima, too ill at the time to pay much heed to
ordinary matters, smiled when she heard of Kurram's request. "So a dove takes his fancy!" And she
added, "Nur Mahal's brother's daughter."

Meanwhile a misadventure had happened to
Jahangir which pleased him greatly. He had been
seized by a whim to hunt and had departed down the
river with an escort of horsemen and a few nobles,
picking up a company of beaters at the edge of the
forest growth.

For some days he amused himself, until Thursday,
which he considered his lucky day. They were hunting with cheetahs, loosing the trained beasts from the
saddle at sight of game, until one of his personal attendants came leaping through the brush crying that
a tiger had been sighted.

[1]Arjamand is better known to history as the Empress Mumtaz-
Mahal, the well loved wife of Shah Jahan (the title name of Prince
Kurram). It was for her body that he built the Taj Mahal.

"*Ai,* my lord, I went beyond the line of beaters, yonder. I saw a tree with kites sitting upon it. I then said to myself I would have a little sport of my own, God willing. Taking out pointless arrows, I strung my bow and went toward them, softly, softly. A bullock's carcase, half eaten, lay in the grass beside me, and from it arose a tiger, huge as a cart. May I never eat again if it is not so."

"And it went, where?" Jahangir demanded. He liked a tiger stalk better than other hunting.

"By Allah, I followed and watched it go into a thicket. I called the beaters who surrounded the place. Listen, now, to the pounding of their sticks, O Lord of my Life."

At a word from Jahangir, the leopards were chained and handed over to the guards, while two heavy matchlocks were brought up with their tripods. The sun was down behind the forest mesh, and less than an hour of light remained, but the emperor and five or six horsemen rode after the guide.

They discovered the tiger standing in the deep shadow of a plane tree, and Jahangir moved closer, taking one of the heavy guns. His horse would not stand at sight of the beast, and he slid from the saddle, running to a bare mound to take better aim. He fired once, unable to make out in the drifting smoke whether he had hit the tiger. At a shot from the second barrel, the beast rose and charged, clawing a huntsman who stood near.

As it did so Jahangir took the other gun from his weapon bearer, Anup Ray, who hastened to place

the tripod before him. Resting the matchlock on this,
Jahangir took aim while Anup Ray held the tripod
firm. But the tiger roared and whirled, charging the
men on the mound beside it. Jahangir shifted his aim
swiftly and fired. The ball smashed through the
tiger's teeth and mouth.

The shock maddened the beast, and the servants
around Jahangir fled, knocking him down and tread-
ing on his body. Anup Ray stood his ground, letting
the tripod slide away, and striking at the beast's head
with his stick. The bloody teeth caught the huntsman's forearms, and Anup Ray went down, as two of
the nobles came up with drawn swords.

They slashed through the dust cloud at the striped
body, until Anup Ray freed his arms, which had
been saved by heavy bracelets—but not before he was
clawed across the shoulder and chest. On his knees,
the huntsman saw the great beast rising at him, and
in desperation grappled the tiger about the body.
Locked together like wrestlers, they rolled down the
slope, to the keen delight of Jahangir, who had been
helped to his feet by now.

A beater ran by them, and the tiger, rising suddenly, struck him with a paw, knocking him dead to
the ground. But Anup Ray drew his sword, slashing
the tiger's eyes, and armed men hastened in to slay
the beast.

Unhurt, Jahangir had followed every motion of
the fight. Indolent as he was, he never lacked courage, nor did he draw back from danger. Once he had
beaten a tiger from the back of an elephant with the

butt of an empty musket. Upon his return to camp he ordered a wine repast to celebrate the hunt, and he wrote down the whole of it in his memoirs.

"As I had seen," he explained to Nur Mahal when he told her the story in the Agra citadel a few days later, "how he offered his life for me, I gave Anup Ray a special sword and increased his yearly pay. I bestowed on him the title of Chief Tiger Slayer."

"And then?" she asked.

"Sunday I passed in fishing, and seven hundred and sixty and six fish were caught." Jahangir always kept count of his bag. "I ate only those with scales, because they do not feed upon the flesh of dead animals. One of my camels was loaded with five heavy nilgaus. And then a poet, Nasiri of Nishapur, came and waited on me. He imitated something of Anwari, in this fashion, *'What matchless beauty this is for the world!'*"

He felt again the almost fierce delight in her which seized him after an absence, as he crushed her in his arms, seeking her lips. Nur Mahal, outwardly attentive to his every word, was pondering the strange nature of men who rejoiced in hunting, and she turned to him suddenly, her eyes softening in appeal.

"Take me with thee, the next time. I have never hunted tiger."

"Thou?" Jahangir smiled. "Could thy hands hold a gun?"

Her slender fingers twined in his, and she nodded gravely. Jahangir could not resist when she begged for something with a child's wistfulness. "Ay so—if my lord is by my side. Have I not held bow and crossbow truly? Surely it would be better sport to aim at a charging beast."

She looked both lovely and expectant as she waited while the emperor pondered. No woman in his memory had attempted such a thing. Still, to have the Persian at his side during the long hours of a stalk, and to watch her try her skill . . . He could bring down the tiger, when she missed, and show his mastery of weapons.

"I know not how it will please thee, heart of mine. But if it be thy wish . . ."

To join together his two passions for a day, that would be a new experience for him. Which was precisely what Nur Mahal wished. Jahangir found the idea so intriguing that he became intent on preparations at once and failed to pay his usual visit of greeting to Prithvi, contenting himself with sending her some of the nilgau horns as trophies.

Within a week Dad-i-Ilahi—God's Gift—the chief elephant of the imperial string, came into the harem outer courtyard with his howdah arranged in strange fashion. Under the rear half of the canopy, curtains had been hung—dark silk veils that could be drawn aside at need to permit a gun to be thrust out.

Since the emperor himself came to the harem court, instead of mounting the elephant as usual in the great central courtyard, women flocked into the galleries to watch. They saw Dad-i-Ilahi kneel by the carpet's end, and Jahangir go to the forepart of the howdah followed by two gun bearers who prostrated themselves when a woman's veiled figure appeared on the carpet and ascended the ladder. She took her place behind the curtains, but not before everyone had recognized Nur Mahal.

The great elephant rose, trumpeting once at a prod from the *mahout*. It was his salutation to Jahangir, and a half dozen other elephants answered from without the wall as the gray beast plodded through the glare of sunlight toward the road.

It was long after dark when the hunters returned and the courtyard became ablaze with torches. Jahangir was smiling as he joined the group of cup companions, Farrash and Nasiri among them, who were to take supper with him that night.

"We found the tiger that had been troubling the peasants and travelers on the river road," he explained. "They had surrounded him, and I told Nur Mahal to shoot at him."

The guests had already heard the tale of the hunt from their servants, but they waited expectantly, observing how Jahangir's dark eyes shone with delight.

"An elephant becomes restless when it smells a tiger," he went on, "and to hit from an imari is difficult. Even Mirza Rustam who is, after me, the best shot, has missed three and four times in succession. Yet Nur Mahal Begam hit and killed this tiger with one shot."

That night Jahangir was in a mood for amusement. After finishing the sherbet and almond cakes that ended the supper, he called for dried grapes and wine. The poets, catching his mood, began to improvise verses, and Nasiri, the youngest, rose from his place and cried aloud that they must have music and girls to dance in such a delightful spot.

"Nay," the emperor objected, "have music if you will, but let the raqqa girls abstain from the society of men."

When the small drums and pipes began to sound plaintively behind the screen—they were seated on one of the roofs with the muslin canopy rolled back—Jahangir had a fresh thought. "Dance thou, O Nasiri of the golden voice. Stay, he must be encouraged. Give him a cup of three-year-old beer."

"And with it, O Lord of Our Lives," put in a courtier, Asaf Khan, "a cup of distilled spirits, to give him strength."

"Motion and strength," Jahangir nodded gravely, "go together."

"The very essence of truth," Farrash chanted. "The very word of Aristotle from the lips of our Pole of Empire."

"I knew it not," Jahangir admitted modestly. "That is, I knew not the saying of Aristotle."

"Then what need have we," Asaf Khan's smooth voice put in, "of the dead Greek philosopher when beside us we have the living fount of Wisdom?"

A chorus of assent greeted this—the other cup companions wishing they had thought first of the compliment. Meanwhile Nasiri had been offered the two cups, and seized them, one in each hand.

"At a draft!" cried Jahangir. "A robe of honor if thou canst dance in time, afterward."

"Salamet padishah!" The young Persian smiled and turned to the north to pour out a few drops, after the old Mongol custom.

"No libations!" Asaf warned him. "Drink all, as was commanded."

Nasiri downed one cup after the other. The blood rushed to his head, and he choked. In time to the beat of the drums, he began to move his feet, patting the supper cloth.

"Faster," urged Asaf who had seen with one eye that Jahangir was losing interest. "By the soul of Balkis, that is a blind beggar's walk."

The mixed drafts were finding their way to Nasiri's head, and he snatched off Asaf's turban, unwinding the long cloth as he circled, and throwing it over his own head like a veil. Although this was sheer insult, Asaf heard Jahangir chuckle and had to force an unwilling smile.

Meanwhile Nasiri's tongue had become loosed, and he sang, clapping his hands in cadence:

> *"The girls of the garden were bright,*
> *Their eyes shone like stars—*
> *Fragrant buds on bending stems,*
> *More than wine they delight*
> *Us, and tie knots*
> *In our hearts."*

He stepped into a dish of raisins, lost his balance —caught at the flying turban cloth, and fell heavily. Jahangir, who had found his antics wearisome, laughed at his fall.

"Lo," he cried, *"wrapped in his shroud, Nasiri goes to his grave."*

"Now," Asaf assented, "we will need another performer."

"Where is that Pathan of thine?" Jahangir demanded. He had a keen memory for many things, and it occurred to him that Asaf Khan had presented to him at one of the private audiences a young warrior from the hills who had sworn that he could use any weapon and strike down any foeman.

"Grandeur of the Empire, he waits with my attendants at the Darwaza Akbar gate, longing for a second sun-illumining glance from the Presence."

"Send for him, and we will make trial of the skill he boasts."

While the talk went on, Jahangir became silent, falling into one of his dark moods. When at last he looked up at the tall Pathan who salaamed gracefully beyond the cloth, he brightened a little. The man had a thin, passionate face framed in oiled tresses under a knotted turban, and his girdle bore knives of a half dozen sizes and shapes. Two *tulwars* hung at his hips, a shield was slung upon his back, and Jahangir wondered if he had not left a musket at the gate.

"Well," he observed, "thou hast weapons enough. What is the price of thy service?"

The Pathan considered coolly. "A hundred gold muhrs a moon, O Shah," he decided, naming a fantastic amount.

"And what," Jahangir demanded curiously, "canst thou do to earn such a sum?"

"I am a champion. With sword or gun or knife or bare hands, ahorse or afoot, in light or in dark, I will stand against any living antagonist. Aye, by Allah, I will cast him down at the feet of your lordship."

Ordinarily Jahangir would have smiled at the naïve bragging of the hillman, who came of a fighting race. Now the black mood was on him, and he rose suddenly. "We will see. You may fight *one* with bare hands and by torchlight. Come."

"As the king commands!" The Pathan tossed his head, and the shield clashed against the mail shirt that covered his body.

With Jahangir leading, the revelers and their attendants left the roof, descending to the great courtyard, and turning into the public garden near the stables. Asaf Khan, seeing that Jahangir was very drunk, called for linkmen to light the way and ordered some soldiers off duty to follow. In one corner of the garden a large bamboo framework had been built to hold any animals that the Mogul might order brought in alive for his inspection. He liked to study them and have them painted.

Before this pen Jahangir came to a halt. "Here is thy foeman," he informed the Pathan, who had kept close behind him. "Make ready."

Peering between the bamboo bars, the warrior saw a lion crouched in the darkest corner, snarling at the torches. The man's eyes opened wide, and his breath hissed between his teeth. To go on foot against a caged lion with sword and shield was to hazard his life. He would be fortunate if he slew the lion and escaped with mangling.

"Put down thy weapons—all of them," Jahangir ordered calmly. "Thou wilt wrestle with this antagonist. So did Anup Ray with the tiger, gaining great reward thereby. If thou canst overcome this one with thy hands, a hundred muhrs a month shall be thy payment."

Uncertainly, the Pathan looked about him. This was surely a jest, but he knew not how to answer it. The revelers and soldiers avoided his glance and moved toward the other sides of the pen. When the linkmen ranged themselves about the bars, the hill-man understood it was not a jest.

"By Ali's breath," he cried, "let me take at least my tulwar!"

"Thou hast heard the order," Asaf Khan muttered. "Be quick."

Slowly the Pathan let his shield fall, and pulled the weapons from his girdle. Sweat from his forehead dripped upon his lips, and his chest heaved. "To hear is—to obey," he whispered. When the keepers lifted the bars from the cage door, he beat his clenched fists once against his chest and ran into the pen.

With a shout he flung himself at the yellow beast. One of his arms was clawed into ribbons by two lightning strokes of a paw; his free hand caught at the lion's throat, and was clamped between gnashing teeth that snapped the bones. The Pathan staggered back, with blood spurting from the torn arm. The maddened lion roared and crouched, its tail sweeping the sand.

Then it rushed, knocking him down, and pulling open his side between ribs and hip.

Jahangir took his eyes from the mangled body.

They were staring and bloodshot in the torchlight,
and they searched the throng behind him until they
fastened upon a stalwart Turk, one of the court
wrestlers. "Thou see'st, Toghrul Bey," he exclaimed.
"The lion hath vanquished this one at thy game. Can
thy hand subdue him?"

Startled, the heavy wrestler salaamed, beating his
forehead against the earth. *"Ai,* my Padishah!"

"Often hast thou made boast of thy strength,
Toghrul Bey. Now is the time to make proof of thy
courage."

The wrestler's head turned from side to side on
the massive neck, and he breathed deep. Again he
salaamed, and rose with dignity, finding his voice
as he did so. "It is for the King to command, for his
servant to obey. Judge, all of ye, of the courage of
Toghrul Bey." He swelled his chest under the
jeweled velvet vest, and rolled back the long sleeves
from his muscular arms.

Indifferent as the fatalist he was, he stepped
through the door when it was opened. Advancing
slowly, his body stooped and his arms bent, he circled
the snarling lion. His round head sank lower into his
shoulders, and his lips drew back in a soundless
grimace.

His bare feet—he had shaken off his slippers—
edged forward into the bloodied sand. Suddenly he
screamed, as the lion whirled and leaped. Dropping
to his knees the wrestler tried to duck under the
sweeping paws and grapple the beast's body. But
one paw smashed down on his shoulder, and the lion,
feeling the man beneath him, clawed savagely with

a hind foot that stripped the flesh from the wrestler's ribs.

There was a flurry of the tawny body, and the flash of fangs in the torchlight. Then the lion ran off, to crouch again, leaving Toghrul Bey moaning on the earth, bitten about the jaw and the chest. He seemed too much hurt to try to crawl to the entrance.

"Still the beast prevails," Jahangir's deep voice proclaimed. "Go in against him—thou!"

Even Farrash and Asaf Khan were silent, and Nasiri forced his way out of the circle of torchlight when a third man, a soldier this time, was ordered into the pen without weapons. Jahangir, still in the grip of the black mood, sat motionless on a carpet that had been spread for him. He did not rise until eleven men had gone into the cage.

Then, in the early hours of the morning, he returned listlessly into the palace, called for opium to drink, and slept in a stupor until the jharoka hour had passed.

The tale of the eleven men who wrestled with the lion went through Agra's citadel that morning, from the gate of the prostitutes that was called the House of Satan to the elephant lines. No one heeded it much —the eleven dead and mangled had been low-born servants of the emperor's will, and in the multitude about the throne fever and poison took heavier toll daily than that. Jahangir's cruelty, inherited equally from his Tartar forbears and his Rajput mother, did not surprise his people. What if he had once watched the skin stripped from a living man, and had ordered another sewn tight in the skin of a newly slain ox—putting him in the heat of the sun until the shrinking hide had tortured him into oblivion? The two had displeased the emperor, who had the whim to punish them in this fashion. At other times his kindness was like the warmth of the sun, giving life to his people.

Yet Nur Mahal became thoughtful when she heard the tale from one of her garment maids. Jahangir, drunk, had ordered his own followers into the cage to satisfy his blood lust, within two hours of the time when in leaving her he had played idly with the pearls that wrapped her throat.

" 'Of night the souls of men from out their cages flee,' " she repeated softly.

"What said the princess?" The garment maid looked inquisitive.

"A riddle, too fine-spun for thee," she smiled. "Why do we change our natures at night, why do we act otherwise than in the day?"

"Perhaps," the girl hazarded, "because it is dark then, and we grow afraid."

"If we do."

The girl looked sideways at her mistress and said nothing. She was a young thing, an orphan, all eyes and gentle laughter. She called herself Maryam, and Nur Mahal had found her astray as a child without a protector. Maryam had grown up in the Persian's service and had become utterly devoted to her. She had been given the responsibility of watching Nur Mahal's jewels.

That evening she hung around the latticed gallery anxiously, making shy attempts to interest her mis-

tress in trinkets or talk. Nur Mahal had one of her
silent spells, in which she would sit by the stone fretwork for hours without moving, lost in dreaming.
Now she rested her forehead against the cool marble
and watched the moonlight strike little gleams from
the ripple of the river. She was weary of the zenana,
very weary of the corridors and the voices that whispered praise of her—and would more eagerly whisper scandal about her at the least provocation. She
knew that she was spied upon, in her rooms, and that
only dread of Jahangir's anger prevented the spies
from inventing tales about her. . . . In the night
there should be respite. . . .

"O heart of mine," she whispered suddenly, "let us
put on the Khan's dress. Just for a little."

It was what Maryam dreaded, and she crept closer,
rigid with protest. "Here? Among these people—O
my lady——"

"Now. Bring it now, with the turban cloth."

Obediently—for it could not enter her small head
to disobey—Maryam went to a teakwood chest hidden in the depths of a dressing room.

"And send word to Arslan to saddle two horses
and lead them for exercise past the jharoka window,"
Nur Mahal added, smiling.

"*Ai-a,* may Allah the Compassionate forbid——"

"Make haste, or he will be gone from the stables."

When Maryam returned from giving the message
to an old slave woman at the door of the apartment,
she found the Persian kneeling by the opened chest,
taking out one garment after another. Carefully,
Maryam drew the curtain behind them and dole-

fully assisted her mistress out of the loose sari. Then she helped her into the first part of the costume, a pair of baggy silk breeches, ankle long. Over the Persian's slender shoulders she drew a light tunic, and over that an embroidered vest. Last of all came a sleeveless *gaba* coat, open in front and reaching to the knees.

On her mistress's feet Maryam placed soft riding slippers, and wound a girdle cloth several times above the hips to hide the too slender waist.

"The daggers," whispered Nur Mahal, stripping off her rings and giving them to the maid.

Maryam searched in the chest and produced a pair of fine Persian blades with carved ivory hilts, in bossed leather sheaths with tassels hanging from the ends. These went into the front of the girdle.

"Now the betel to chew, like a true *ahadi*. My teeth must not be too white—hast thou any of the stain?"

While she chewed vigorously at the betel leaves, the maid rubbed a dampened cloth over the lower part of her face and her throat, even under the hair, until the clear skin became yellow-brown, as if burned by the sun. With a pencil of dark grease Maryam traced lines under the bright eyes. "But the turban," she whispered fearfully. "Let me do it now. It is too great a task for one alone in the dark."

"Yet alone I must be."

Taking the yards of white silk on her arm, Nur Mahal scanned herself in a silver mirror attentively, pulled up the girdle a trifle. "Now the woman's robe," she said at last.

Maryam put over her shoulders an outer robe of

common dark muslin, drawing a fold of it over the luxuriant hair, and hanging a heavy veil carefully above her mistress's ears so that only the eyes were visible.

"It is madness, this," she sighed. "May Allah have thee in his keeping."

"Wait thou by the door of the sleeping room, heart of mine, until I come again."

With that Nur Mahal slipped away into the darkness. No one was at the door of her apartment, and she waited until the corridor was free before venturing out. A few quick steps, and she reached the head of a dark stair. Out of the gloom below her, two green eyes gleamed and vanished—shone again as she started involuntarily, the blood leaping in her veins. It was an animal, of course, and there could be only one four-legged thing in the harem with eyes so wide and menacing.

"So, little brother," she whispered, "thou art caged and restless in the night!"

Descending boldly, she felt Prithvi's leopard rub caressingly against her knee. The great cat that had sensed her fear of a moment before was now in some way aware of her recognition. Then the gloom of the narrow stair gave way to candlelight, and Nur Mahal looked down upon a landing where two stalwart Afghan women sprawled at ease with knives in their girdles. For a while the Persian watched them, as women came down another stair and crossed the landing, stepping between the guards. These women were servants, going to the lower floor, and the Afghans only glanced up at them casually. At this landing the living quarters of the harem ended; below were only the many kitchens and wash rooms and the sleeping places of the thousands of workers.

When the group of sturdy Moslem slaves appeared on the landing, Nur Mahal stepped down behind them. With heavy tread she passed between the guards, descending into a labyrinth of corridors that smelt of steaming rice and wet garments. No one glanced at her twice as she made her way out of the crowds toward the storerooms.

Strong-limbed peasant women passed her, carrying sacks or baskets, and she traced them to cool vaulted rooms piled with grains and fruits. Because tons of foodstuffs moved daily into the harem kitchens, and because the peasant girls came and went continuously, sleeping apparently not at all, the wide low gate into the outer courtyard stood open. Nur Mahal edged toward it, listening to sounds in the courtyard, where black Abyssinian swordsmen should be on guard. When she heard their high-pitched voices at a little distance, she stepped through the stone gate into the deep shadow of the wall. The black guards squatted in the moonlight, a pebble's toss away.

For an instant the Persian hesitated. She could step back into the storeroom, retrace her path in safety to her rooms. If she went beyond this point she broke pardah—seclusion—and if she were recognized her life would be at stake. But the cool moonlight drew her toward it, and she could hear the breath of the night wind in the garden beyond.

Swiftly she threw off the black muslin overdress

and coiled her hair tight upon her head. Picking up the long strip of turban cloth she began to wind it upon the hair, wrapping it deftly, fold upon fold, until she could knot it and let the free end dangle by her cheek. She even fastened a turquoise bangle above her forehead.

It was difficult work without a mirror or a friend's hand to guide the folds, but she had done it often. As a girl she had gone on nightly rides with tolerant Ghias Beg, her father—who had even ventured to take her out, in boy's garments during the day. In India the veiled women could not appear in public on a horse—they must travel in litters or *palkis,* and Nur Mahal had found no joy in lying behind a screen. After her marriage, during the long absences of her soldier husband, she had made nightly forays into the outer world dressed as a man, attended by her servant Arslan. She had dared make up as an *ahadi*—a gentleman trooper, wandering in search of service—and visit the camps of grandees who had halted in the neighborhood. Once, to his consternation, she had dropped in on her father, and once she had spent several days in the quarters of Mahabat Khan, the War Lord, the Afghan who was the first general of the empire. She had enjoyed listening to the talk of Mahabat Khan, who like herself had been born in the western hills, and who dared speak the truth at all times. . . .

Hastily Nur Mahal hid the woman's garment and veil behind some bags of sesame seed. Keeping to the shadow of the wall and moving without a sound, she reached one of the courtyard entrances and walked through it without pretense of concealment. In the moonlight she looked like any one of a thousand young gentlemen who served the court without care or overmuch money.

When she passed the guard at the outer wall, someone jested idly: "Was *she* not kind—that the young lord goes so early?"

"May jahannum take all girls," Nur Mahal responded huskily. "May they sleep on thorns and eat of the bitterness they give to us."

The voice laughed in sympathy. "True—they are all alike. One hour honey and the next sour beer."

Without haste she wandered forth on the sandy plain that still gave out the heat of the day, until a rider trotted up with a led horse, and dismounted in the moonlight a dozen paces from her.

"Is it Khalil Khan?" a deep voice asked uncertainly.

"As thou see'st, Arslan. Nay—" for the old Turk who had come from the hills with Ghias Beg threw himself down before her and lifted her foot, placing it on his head—"do not so! The years have not changed thee. Say, is my turban as it should be?"

Timidly Arslan surveyed her. She had played with the metal boxes hanging from his waistcloth when she had been a child, and now she was a sultana of the empire. He knew that, if she were recognized in his company, he would be given to the elephants to tread upon, if he escaped the hands of the torturers. His own peril Arslan viewed with the eye of a fatalist, but his calm was upset by the sight of this

woman, who belonged now to the Mogul, alone and
outside the citadel gates. His voice faltered as he
answered, "The turban? I see naught amiss, but
why——"

"Why stay within walls when God's earth is wide!"
Nur Mahal cried, and took the rein of the led horse,
swinging into the saddle. "Tell me the news of the
camps."

Agra's bazaar, outside the west gate of the citadel
where the three bronze mortars stood, was still alight
and crowded at the fourth hour of the night. Men
who had slept through the heat of the day had come
forth to eat and gossip. They squatted among piles of
carpets or jars of oil, and talked in many languages.

At one corner a Turk from Istanbul sat behind a
water pipe, puffing at intervals upon the amber
mouthpiece and blowing a cloud of smoke from his
lips, to the astonishment of the crowd about him.
When he did so the water bubbled in the jar.

"Yah tabak," he explained with dignity. "The
tobacco. See, it burns in this small tower. The smoke
of it soothes the mind and heals afflictions of the
belly. There is no harm. Any one of you may draw
in a draft of the smoke—thus—for a quarter rupee
piece."

"*Wah*—that is magic. All magic harms, in time."

"No, by Allah, it is not magic. It is a new art,
known only to certain skilled physicians."

"God knows. But surely there is a devil in the red
fire. Dung does not burn like that."

Several voices cried assent, because the onlookers had noticed how the tobacco glowed and sank into ashes.

"Perhaps," the Turk admitted, "a devil may be in the fire. But, look ye, my brothers, when the smoke of it passes through the water, the devil is slain, and the smoke heals thereafter. For a quarter rupee ye may make trial of it."

His voice was drowned by the shrill cries of beggars besieging a horseman. A hawk seller holding hooded gerfalcons on a perch elbowed his way through the throng, sworn at viciously by some wandering Rajputs who made pretense of being contaminated by his touch. A Hindu ascetic in a salmon-colored robe edged past them, his eyes watching the ground mechanically, lest he tread on some living insect or filth. He held a begging bowl, half filled, and muttered acknowledgment when a moist ball of rice was dropped into his bowl.

He glanced curiously, without turning his head, at a strange figure on a ragged carpet. A man in leather breeches and boots, his long hair bound by a scarf. On the carpet before him, an old ship's compass. Arranged about the compass were pages torn from a Bible, rich with illuminations.

"Doctor of the stars am I," the stranger intoned in bad Hindi. "I read Fate. See, these pieces of the zodiac." He pointed at the illuminations and added, "Doctor of the stars—fate for a rupee."

Passers-by paused, interested in the curious round box with the needle that always pointed one way, no matter how the box was turned. The man was a

Portuguese sailor, who had wandered in from the coast and had set up shop as an astrologer.

Two Jesuits in long black robes and sandals came swinging by, and stopped to exclaim angrily at the torn Bible. "What manner of astrologer art thou, blasphemer!"

"One fit enough," the sailor leered, in his own speech, "for these dogs of heretics."

Through the alleys Nur Mahal rode, sniffing half-forgotten odors, and picking up threads of talk at random from the open booths. Here was the heart of the outer world, within touch of her. While he kept off the beggars with the tip of his sheathed scimitar, Arslan pointed out new sights to her. The gray turbans of bearded Afghans, stuffing themselves with forbidden sausages—the cavalcade of Sayyids of Barha, in their silvered mail and scarlet cloaks, the finest horsemen of the army—the group of hatchet-faced Arab merchants, up from Surat with dyed cotton from Egypt.

Coming out of the street of the cotton sellers, Nur Mahal reined in her pony sharply. A dozen horsemen were approaching at a trot, the outriders carrying torches, and all of them careless of anything that might be in their way. Behind the torchbearers were two officers, one—by token of the robe of honor he wore and the white horse tails hanging from either side his saddle—of high rank. She recognized Mahabat Khan, the Afghan general. In the five years since she had seen him, his tall figure had grown thinner, but his beard jutted out from his chin, and he wore his turban a little to one side, just as she remembered.

She would have drawn back into the bazaar street, but a pair of yoked bullocks pushed her horse from behind, and she was forced a pace forward. An outrider shouted at her impatiently and swung his torch almost in her eyes. Her horse tossed its head and swerved, as Arslan reined his horse angrily before her.

"Is the way not wide enough, O hill dog, that thou shouldst bark at this lord?"

Mahabat Khan glanced toward them, and pulled in, ordering his men to halt. He looked at Nur Mahal so long that Arslan clenched his hand upon his sword hilt.

"By God's mercy," the general exclaimed, "here is Khalil Khan, still a trooper."

"Ay, Sirdar," she murmured, bending her head, "Khalil Khan salaams before your honor."

"Seekest thou me? What service hast thou?"

"I have service at court."

The veteran Afghan still considered the slender trooper curiously. He had an excellent memory for faces. "Ride a little with me," he urged brusquely. "The war in thine old subah of Bengal has ended."

Perforce she moved to his side, and the cavalcade resumed its trot, while Arslan, troubled, fell in close behind his mistress. Nur Mahal had heard that the great Afghan had been called to Agra for a conference, and that he had sat that evening with the Mogul and Kurram. She rode in silence, her eyes half closed against the torchlight, wondering what had been discussed in the Shah's tower, and only certain of the fact that Mahabat Khan was in a dark humor.

"The Sirdar hath grown in honor during these years," she hazarded.

"By God," growled the Khan, "I have grown gray in service. I have sat on my haunches like a pregnant woman—waiting." He chewed his beard, meditating. "Our Lord the Padishah hath the heart of a soldier, yet who gives orders? The Treasurer of the Army! The Governor of Bengal! The women behind the curtain!"

He nodded toward the two inner towers of the citadel, dim against the stars. Few would have spoken aloud of the Mogul's women, but Mahabat Khan was both hostile to all women of the court, and indifferent to consequences.

Gravely Nur Mahal assented. "It was otherwise in Akbar's day."

"What knowest thou of that, youngling? Thy beard is not to be seen, yet."

"But, O Sirdar, I have heard the talk."

"Ay, the talk. The plans of this one, and the counter plans of that one. I have heard overmuch of it. What sayeth Muhammad—peace be upon him? 'Listen to the advice of a woman, and then do the contrary of what she advises.'"

Nur Mahal checked a ripple of laughter. "It is written as the Sirdar saith. Fortunate, indeed, for the court that Mahabat Khan commands on the frontiers, for victory comes always to his sword— even after overmuch talk and bad advice. Now, my

lord, I must draw my rein aside." She smiled at him
swiftly. "I have duty before me this night."

When she had departed down a side street with
her follower, Mahabat Khan turned to his officer.
"What think ye of that ahadi?"

"He sits the saddle in odd fashion."

"It is easy to talk to him." The Afghan tugged at
his beard and smiled. "By Allah's mercy, had I not
been a virtuous man five years ago, I could have
loved that youth."

Meanwhile the comely youth in question galloped
down an alley, with Arslan muttering behind her.
Nur Mahal knew that too much time had passed—
barely four hours remained before the first light,
when she must be in her own apartment again. Her
heart throbbed heavily, in time with the hoofbeat of
the horse, and she felt her throat and cheeks grow
warm. She was late, but she could have a precious
hour at the rendezvous she sought through the
labyrinth of dark streets where the gates of the *serais*
stood closed and guarded, and the porticoes of the
mosques were dark.

"Take care," Arslan whispered.

A mounted patrol appeared ahead of them with
its lanterns, and they turned aside, winding between
blank walls that yielded to the fresher air and the
gardens of a suburb. Presently Nur Mahal pulled
her horse in and looked at the houses on either side.
No lights showed, and certainly no one was afoot at
that hour.

At the door of a stone dwelling, white under the
moonlight, she dismounted and called softly, while

Arslan drew the horses prudently into shadow. In a moment a woman's veiled head appeared over the parapet of the roof.

"What is this? We be poor folk!"

"Be at peace, Ayesha. It is Khalil Khan and one who tends the horses. Open quickly."

The woman's head vanished with a gasp, and bare feet pattered down to the door. A man's voice growled a question, and the darkness within the house became astir. Then bars were lifted down and the door flung open. A stout Moslem woman cast herself down before Nur Mahal, patting the slender riding slippers. *"Ai,* Heaven-born!"

"Hush. Where shall I go?"

"The roof—it is empty except for the one thou— the Sultana seeks."

Pushing past her, Nur Mahal made her way to invisible stairs and climbed to the carpeted roof where cushions had been spread under a thin canopy. From below, the voice of the woman Ayesha sounded in subdued excitement. *"Hai,* ye oxen, get ye gone! The Heaven-born is within the walls, and ye loiter like buffalo getting up from sleep. O that I had men for brothers and not witless snorers. Ye were not so slow to run when the searchers came for men to serve in the cavalry. Have ye not heard me say that the Sultana hath come——"

"Yea," grumbled a deep voice, "and so hath the street heard by now. Still thy cackle—we come."

Two men went out the front door, pulling shawls over their shoulders. Coughing and spitting, they heard Ayesha's warning hiss behind them and moved

out of the moonlight into the shadows, where they
fell into low talk with Arslan. They served Ghias
Beg, as he did.

On the roof Nur Mahal ran to the canopy and
caught within her arms the slender body of a child
waking from sleep. Bewildered, and then smiling,
the girl stared at her. "Heaven-born——"

"Thy mother, Lardili. O child of my heart, thy
mother!"

Nur Mahal threw off the turban, and the flood of
her dark hair fell upon her shoulders, against the
girl's cheek. Lardili thought that it smelled nicely
of rose leaves, and that her mother's hands, running
over her body and pressing her head, were warm and
gentle.

Apart from them, still breathing quickly from excitement, Ayesha knelt, taking care not to look directly into Nur Mahal's eager face. True, this was
Lardili's mother—this sultana of the empire. But
the exalted lady was also a widow, and Ayesha knew
that it brought bad luck to look into the eyes of a
widow. And, fingering her rosary, she prayed that
no misfortune might come to the child.

In silence Nur Mahal rode back to the citadel, and
in spite of Arslan's urging, she took her time in
reaching the bazaar gate. She felt tired, when she
mustered a smile bidding him farewell.

"Look to thyself well," he whispered—in the darkness he still thought of the woman as Mihri—"for
it is at the end, when all appears safe, that danger
comes."

Behind Nur Mahal the sky was lightening, and
the walls began to take shape against the ground as
she crossed the central plaza and threaded her way
through the gardens. The courtyard of the Abys-
sinians loomed dark, except for the lantern of the
guard. Only one man was awake by the light, and
she was able to find her woman's robe and veil without attracting his attention; nor did he see the dark
figure that slipped into the storeroom entrance behind him.

Already the slave women were stirring about the
kitchen fires, and Nur Mahal escaped notice as she
climbed the stairs to the corridor and her own apartment. When she stepped through the curtains of her
sleeping room, Maryam wept with relief, telling her
that nothing had happened here during the night.

Stripped of Khalil Khan's dress and make-up,
Nur Mahal lay down on her quilt. Drowsy with
weariness, she fell asleep at the moment the muezzin
was intoning the morning call to prayer. . . .

A touch on her feet awakened her. The morning
sun burned against the curtain, and the air was hot.
Beside her knelt Maryam with a woman attendant,
both pale with fear. When she sat up the woman
began to beat her forehead against the tiles of the
floor.

"*Ai-a,* the Heaven-born must rouse herself. A girl
of Prithvi's, a painted slut, waited in the corridor at
sunrise, for no good purpose. She saw a youth without a sword enter these chambers—a strange warrior, unknown to her. So, at least, she swears by her
ill-omened gods—even that he wore a Persian tur-

ban and riding slippers. By the night lamp she saw
it. She hath carried her tale to the chief eunuchs,
who have taken her to the Padishah, our master."

"She saw what?"

"It was Khalil Khan," whimpered Maryam.

Nur Mahal stripped a silk bracelet from her
wrist, a slight thing with pearl shell bangles that
Jahangir had given her. "Take this to the Padishah
at once," she ordered. "By a faithful hand, it must
go to his hand—now."

"With what message, Princess?"

She shook her head. "I send no word. The bracelet
he will know."

While her women scurried about like frightened
birds, Nur Mahal let herself be dressed and occupied herself quietly in arranging a tablecloth for
two on the latticed gallery. She had marigold buds
and jasmine brought in, to decorate the cloth, and
seemed not at all disturbed when Jahangir did not
appear until the noon hour.

He came in moodily and waited for her to salute
him, which was unusual. His heavy cheeks were
dark, and his eyes bloodshot with wakefulness and
drink—so her first swift glance told her. And he
seemed ill-content when she asked him how the
meeting with Mahabat Khan in the Shah's tower
had pleased him.

"God knows," he said grimly, "I have heard little
to please me in these last hours. Among other things
a certain girl hath dared to swear by Siva's head
that a man who was no kin of thine or mine visited

thee before the hour of waking, this morning. I
would have had her scourged, but—but——"

When he hesitated, Nur Mahal answered swiftly,
"Others urged upon my lord that it might be true.
And doth the Padishah believe them?"

Jahangir's dark eyes flashed. "Am I one to listen
to slaves' talk? I came hither to tell thee of it and to
know the cause of the talk. Thy moods are wild
enough at times, O light of my life."

For an instant she wondered at the tone and at the
thought behind it. His indolent and matter-of-fact
mind was usually an open book to her, yet at times
she caught glimpses of hidden feelings.

"Then will I show thee the truth." A fleeting
smile caressed him. "If my lord will sit in patience
for one short ghari."

It was more than any twenty-four minutes that
Jahangir waited. But Maryam and other girls
brought him sherbet and food of the kind he liked,
and he refreshed himself—listening presently to the
soft stroking of a *vina* somewhere behind the screens.
He had an ear for music, and he assured himself that
this was a gay little tune.

When the musician entered, the guitar over one
arm, and seated himself gravely on the cushions
near the emperor, Jahangir looked as amazed as a
child. Nur Mahal had made herself up as Khalil
Khan, even to the turban and the riding slippers, and
had added the guitar. He had not known she could
play like this.

"A cup for the Lord of Our Lives," she cried to
her maids. "Will you drink, O King, with such a cup

companion as this?" Lightly her eyes met his, and her slim fingers ran across the vina's strings:

> *"Joyous and gay*
> *Is this, our day,*
> *And the hour*
> *We steal away——"*

Jahangir sipped his wine, listening avidly to the low voice that stirred him so pleasantly. Before the song was half finished, she put aside the guitar and nodded at him with a grimace.

"That was Khalil Khan, thy cup companion. Is not the disguise perfect? Could I not draw the heart out of a timid girl by singing to her beyond a garden wall?"

"Ay, so," he assented approvingly. "I would like to listen to such a wooing."

"At least, I fooled the Hindu girl who saw me walking the corridor in this garb before the dawn prayer."

Jahangir glanced at her quickly and smiled. "Eh, my soul—thou wert making ready to entertain me."

"Making ready," she said quietly, "to amuse my lord. And why not?" Suddenly she lifted her head. "That Hindu girl is outside, under guard. Send for her, to say if this be truly the man she saw."

Although he shook his head, Jahangir yielded to her urgency. The woman, a bath maid of Prithvi, was brought in by an Abyssinian eunuch, and when she rose from her salaam, she cried out in fear, rec-

JAHANGIR

From a contemporary miniature

AKBAR   NUR MAHAL   SHAH JAHAN

PRINCE PARVIZ, SON OF JAHANGIR

FROM "MINIATURE PAINTING OF PERSIA, INDIA AND TURKEY," BY F. R. MARTIN

ognizing Nur Mahal in the guise of the man she had denounced, at Prithvi's insistence.

"Speak, thou! Am I the one?"

The girl shrank back hopelessly. "Thou—art the one."

"See thou," Jahangir instructed the eunuch, "that she is lashed, and tied up in the sun of the inner court."

"But why, my lord?" Nur Mahal demanded instantly. "She told the truth, and was it not in your service?" She turned to the excited Abyssinian. "My lord doth not wish her scourged. Take her back to the dancer, Prithvi, with the word that Nur Mahal hath spared her."

When Jahangir made no objection, the girl was taken away, and at a sign from Nur Mahal her attendants withdrew. Slowly the Persian unwound the turban cloth. For a moment she listened, to make sure that they were alone. Then with a single movement she nestled against him, her lips touching his throat softly, the scent of roses in his nostrils. When he spoke, her low voice echoed utter content, but with every instinct alert her mind was searching into the man beside her, groping for the thought that remained unuttered in the tired brain. She had had a glimpse of something beyond and remote from his passion for her.

He might suspect that she had deceived him—unknowing, he might suspect. Without doubt her enemies in the harem would ransack the citadel for trace of the doings of Khalil Khan; they could discover that she had broken her seclusion by going through the outer gate. Perhaps they would track her into the bazaar, and the tale of her night ride, magnified by wit as delicate as a needle point, would reach his ears little by little in just the way best suited to rouse his suspicions. And poison was not more deadly within the harem than suspicion. . . .

She made up her mind with a little inward breath. "Thy slave," she whispered, "hath broken pardah."

"What slave?" he asked idly.

"This one." From under dark lashes she searched his face intently. "In these garments I rode through Agra last night, returning before the dawn, when that maid saw me."

His body stiffened, and he looked absurdly astonished. *"Thou*—what new jest is this?"

"The truth, O my loved one. It was a mood that came upon me, and I went. The people know nothing of it, and no man touched me."

"But—without me, into the city—why?"

"Perhaps the night called me. I have never been shut within walls before."

Jahangir had more than his share of pride; he was the son of a conqueror, remotely above his subjects. Not even the Tartar queens had dared challenge his will, and he could not realize at once that this woman had left the precincts of the harem, of her own will, alone and in spite of all the guards. When he did realize it, the blood rushed into his throat, and his heavy lips twitched.

"Do you say 'perhaps' to me? I asked why?"

Fleetingly Nur Mahal thought of the hour on the

roof with Lardili under the setting moon—a thing
Jahangir could never understand, and that she would
not tell him. "It was a mood, a feeling. It comes on
me at times," she said unevenly.

"Perhaps the stake of the inner courtyard will cure
you of it, if you are tied there in the sun, for the
women who have some shame to mock."

The dark eyes of the Persian blazed from her
white face. "Let Akbar's son command it! Am I not
his slave? He can order his men to feed a lion with
their flesh. Ay, and lure himself to sleep with opium
while his armies wait unheeded. Mahabat Khan lied
when he said that you had a soldier's heart."

The sudden bitterness of it struck deep into his
pride. She had cried out involuntarily, meaning
every word of it. Her anger had risen against his,
and for a moment he was speechless. Then a sweep
of his powerful arm cast her back against the cushions, and he drew the jeweled dagger that he always
wore in his girdle.

At sight of the steel blade, above her, Nur Mahal
shrank into herself, swift agony darting through
her, to her finger ends. She did not move or cry out,
and underneath the chill of terror crept a warmth
of feeling. Of release and comfort—that she would
be gone, out of the walls of this room, out of herself.
She did not see the bright steel any longer, and she
did not know that her eyes, shadowed with dread,
stared beyond Jahangir.

But she heard him cry one word, and again, bewildered: "Mihri."

Into the face of the woman had come the fear of

the girl who had struggled in his arms by the garden pool. Jahangir found that the knife in his hand was trembling. He looked at it a moment and put it back, with some difficulty, into its sheath. The pulse that had hammered at his temples died away.

He felt tired, and he had trouble in drawing his breath. Why, he had almost slain Nur Mahal, when her eyes glowed like a panther's in the night. He would have hurt her.

"It is hard to breathe," he complained.

She clapped her hands together, and when a maid came into the gallery bade the girl bring cool Shiraz wine. She filled a crystal cup and held it so that he could drink without moving. Sitting by him, she waited for him to speak, and he stretched out his hand, caressing her throat. How near he had been to slaying her.

"Today," he said moodily, "I am tired. Sing thou to me—I had little sleep before the first light."

Nur Mahal settled back on the cushions, taking up the guitar. Then she laid it aside, and a half-smile touched her lips. " 'Of nights the souls of men from out their cages flee . . .' "

When Jahangir left her apartment he paused instinctively in the corridor, missing his usual draft of opium. He knew what women would have it ready for him. Their slaves would fly about him silently, taking off his clothes, rubbing his body with pounded sandalwood and perfumed water. They would rub his hands and feet, while he listened to music and drank the opium with *falanja* seeds. With cooling oil on his forehead he could lie there and rest.

Still, the afternoon private council would be assembled by now, waiting his arrival. He remembered that the Portuguese envoy had promised the gift of a clock having a painted face and chimes. Reluctantly he turned toward the Queen's Hall and the outer curtain.

It pleased Salima, who had had nothing to distract her for a long time, to consider herself dying. Feeling strangely listless, she found a new diversion in the arguments with the court physicians who came in procession to advise her from the other side of a heavy curtain.

Some told her to swallow pellets made of paper upon which prayers or charms had been written; some—and she dismissed them with high words— wanted to purge her and bring her to a fever sweat with hot poultices and infusions of tea. She allowed the most flattering of them to bleed her, but she gave royal presents to all of them, and listened with satisfaction to the condolences of Ruqaiya her best-loved enemy among the dowagers.

"When thou hast departed to the mercy of God, O most sublime of sultanas," Ruqaiya chanted—since her visit was one of ceremony—"we will be deprived of the Sun of Our Well-being and the Light of Wisdom without which the court and the empire will be darkened by dissension."

"True," Salima assented placidly. "There is no one to take my place. Even thou, O most beloved, will be confounded."

The Tartar widow nodded her well-kept head. "It

is so. At thy time, of seventy and six years, the years cease to be, and the moons come not. Allah grants only the suns of a few more days."

Tears filled her eyes—she was only five years younger than Salima—and she sighed without bitterness. For the moment she forgot Salima's pet fiction, that her age was no more than sixty. And Ruqaiya discovered that she herself had no desire, now that the event was at hand, to become the head of the harem and assume all the thousand duties the elder woman had discharged without apparent effort for a generation.

Salima Sultana sniffed. Although she might be listless, nothing ailed her mind, and she had no sympathy with tears.

"These hakims have no wisdom," she murmured. "What need have I of poultices and tea? I would like to smell once more the air of our hills. And— and to eat a cold melon from the vines of Kabul."

It was her nearest approach to self-pity. But from the hour of Ruqaiya's condolence, she took new interest in what she believed to be her deathbed. The physicians were ordered off, and aged women given permission to begin the wailing. For hours they knelt outside her door chanting the sonorous Arabic verses of the Koran, while former maids and serving women—grandmothers now, for the most part—assembled mysteriously in the harem and took the tasks from the hands of younger women. Even the Abyssinian and Bengali eunuchs ran at their bidding, and the corridors were in an uproar, while at times Salima's caustic voice was heard complaining that the wailing faltered. She had always liked noise and movement, so long as she herself was the center of it.

With her cheeks tinted, and her thin arms weighted down by bracelets, Salima Sultana Begam lay in state, sleeping apparently not at all, her sunken eyes clear and inquisitive. As she remembered old servitors and widows of men who had been slain in her service, one by one, she summoned them, or their daughters, and bestowed upon them horses, cattle, villages, rents and river tolls. To Tartar noblewomen she gave away imperial elephants, shining diadems and single jewels worth the ransom of their husbands, while the eunuch who was treasurer-in-chief of the harem wrote down the bequests and mopped his forehead with his turban end.

"I can take nothing out of the world with me," she assured him impatiently when he ventured to object that she was giving away more than she owned. "The Padishah will attend to it that these small gifts are paid. By God, is it not better that my people should have them than circumcised dogs such as thou?"

The *hakims* told Jahangir that she was not really dying. Her weakness, they said, was caused by a complication of the spleen which they had healed by bleeding. Still, he came dutifully to pay his respects in the evening, to listen when she was moved to talk.

"Shaikhu Baba," she observed once, "you will bury me in the Mandakar rose garden that I caused to be made by the river. You have forgotten that your revered father was accustomed to come there to sit."

"Yes, Perfection of Beauty."

But the old Tartar's mind had wandered back into the past.

"You were born in this hot country, Old Daddy," she mused. "Yet the lords of men your ancestors came from the cold deserts. Did not the first of them who was Chingiz Khan[1] come from the desert to conquer Cathay and all the world? It is so. . . . I have heard that his grandson Khubilai Khan[1] rode into battle upon a throne standing on three elephants. He moved his reigning city out of the deserts into Cathay, and the children of his loins grew weak. . . . Already that flower Arjamand feels life under her heart by Kurram, but I will not live to see the child, her child. *Hai,* she goes with Kurram, like his shadow, to the camp of war. That is the way of thy house. The sultans and emperors, thine ancestors, took the one favorite wife with them—since the day of Chingiz. They lived in the saddle, and they were conquerors . . . forget it not, Shaikhu Baba."

"A wise man once said you can conquer an empire in the saddle, but you may not rule it so."

Salima lay quiet for a moment. "Verily, Old Daddy, you belong to this hot land. It is not like our hills. Was not Chingiz wise? I do not know. . . . He said, Let the throne go to the eldest of the four sons; let all religions be alike, under your rule; live with the army, not in a palace. Such is the law of Chingiz Khan. . . . Did not the Lord of the Planets, Timur, follow it? He also was a conqueror. And the revered Babar, grandsire of thy father, came down

[1] So the name Genghis Khan was pronounced in Asia. Khubilai is more often written Kubla Khan by Europeans

from Samarkand into Hindustan. He made this his home, although his heart went back to the hills again. Like mine—*Ai-a,* like mine. They did not forsake the lashgar, the armed camp, to live their days in a palace. Nor did my lord thy father who made firm the empire of the Mogul."

"And I have kept it as he left it."

"True—true. Yet thou alone wert born to the throne. The others spent their lives in the taking, and making firm. And I know not if it is good to change from their road. I know not. In this hot land there be overmany peoples, with customs differing from ours."

For a moment she pondered, the thin fingers trembling against the quilt.

"Keep thou to the law of Chingiz Khan, Old Daddy. I fear for thee—there be so many about thee, grasping at the edge of thy coat. Who among thy women keeps to the law of the Tartars? Of the great amirs only two remember the law, as it should be remembered—that Afghan, Mahabat Khan, and Shaikh Farid. Do not forget—do not forget. . . . Now I have spoken enough, and I am tired."

A few days later when Jahangir was absent on a hunting expedition, to the surprise of everyone but herself, Salima Sultana Begam was seized by the last agonies and died. Jahangir gave command that she should be buried in the Mandakar garden, and he wrote in his memoirs:

"Seldom were her ability and energy found among women. She received mercy in the sixtieth year of her age, when I was marching from the Dahrah. Accordingly I sent Ghias Beg to bury her in the garden she herself had made."

Her place as leader of the harem became vacant. The court waited for the announcement that Ruqaiya had become mistress behind the curtain, until Jahangir said that the Persian, Nur Mahal, would be the first lady of the harem.

III

"AH, WELL," Farrash observed, "at last we move."

"We move slowly," Nasiri qualified, "as great masses must."

"Yet behold, we arrive."

"Each day we arrive somewhere; however, only God knows where we shall be, in the end."

"God has nothing to do with it." Farrash, who posed as a Sufi or mystic, was in reality a freethinker and liked to argue that he was sure of nothing except the functions of his own body. He also quoted a little known poet, Omar of the Tentmakers. "You say Allah, I say Khoda, others say Yahweh, and some others Brahma. As for these Hindus they have so many names of gods it makes my head ache to recall them. But Jahangir the Mogul is the one who directs our steps—where he wishes to go, we will go. And, what is more, you know it."

Nasiri smiled. "But I do not know who directs the mind of Jahangir."

This was dangerous ground, and Farrash became cautious. They were sitting their horses in a wide plain of trampled millet, with throngs of camp servants hurrying around them. The servants had ears, and it was one of the poet's axioms that every word spoken may be heard by somebody. "At present," he parried, "our master hath war and journeys in his mind, and hunting, as ever. He hath the menagerie on wheels, and painters to paint animals. He plays at being Akbar, conquering the Rajput rajas in their hills. We must infuse our verses with martial motives, O Nasiri."

"I think he seeks to give Prince Kurram his annointment of blood. The prince is able in commanding, with the help of the Khan Khanim. Yet only Mahabat Khan can accomplish much against the rajas, and he hath been sent, as usual, to do border patrol."

"Nasiri, thou knowest not this imperial court of ours as I do. If Mahabat Khan commanded the new army of conquest and won great victories, what credit would fall to Kurram? On the other hand if, given a huge army, Kurram wins a little victory, he will be given great credit. 'Tis clear as mathematics. Jahangir plays at war for the moment. So bethink thee of rhymes that will make resounding victories out of little battles, and be content, as I am."

"Ay," Nasiri smiled, "for that is what you **do** best."

Farrash shrugged. "It is what I am paid for." He

glanced through the drifting dust clouds. "Still, there was never anything quite like this pageant—unless the host of Xerxes."

Around them on the plain, a city of tents had grown up within a few hours. That morning the quartermaster of the court had marked out the encampment, selecting first the great square for the Mogul's quarters. Around this a wall of cotton cloth and bamboo had been put up.

Within this wall, Farrash could see the roofs of red pavilions, swaying under the wind gusts. He could distinguish the long council pavilions and the Mogul's sleeping tent, with the pavilions of women of the harem behind it.

Near at hand, where the gateway of the imperial enclosure rose with its snapping banners, the stirrup artillery had come in. Fifty light brass cannon were being wheeled to either side the gate in a tumult of shouting and a thudding of hoofs while the Lord Thunder Thrower, the Turk who was chief of the artillery, watched impassively. From the distant line of the canebrake appeared a file of elephants, dust coated, chewing bits of sugar cane and long grass. By their steel-tipped tusks and leather housings, Farrash recognized the war elephants. Scores of them swayed through the confusion of the plain to their allotted lines.

At gunshot distance from the imperial enclosure, the camps of the Rajput princes, the Pathan lords and the high dignitaries of the court were being set up. Along the main avenue of approach the bazaar people were busied at their booths, while their fami-

lies swarmed in and out of the bullock carts behind
them. Already smoke and steam drifted up from the
public bathhouse, and beyond it rose the makeshift
tower of the traveling mosque.

From time to time the clash of cymbals or a fresh
outbreak of shouting heralded the arrival of a lord
with his horsemen and a small army of servants trail-
ing behind, followed by the families of the troopers.
As the sun dropped lower, the tumult began to die
down. Grooms were rubbing the horses in the picket
lines, while boys scurried past with dripping water
skins. The last strings of baggage camels plowed
through the tents and knelt, disappearing from sight
but not from hearing as their loads were taken off.
The breeze lessened to a breath of warm air.

Wand-bearers appeared in the main avenue, waving the people toward the tents.

"Make way for the coming of the Padishah. 'Way
for the Shadow of God."

The two poets dismounted, leaving their horses
with their grooms, and forced a passage through the
gathering throng to the gate of the imperial quarters.
With critical appreciation they watched a body of
Rajput cavalry trot into the avenue and wheel the
horses to form on either side, with a clattering of
lance shafts against shields and a tossing of crested,
silvered helmets.

"Is this a court," Nasiri wondered, "or an army on
the march?"

"It is the lashgar, the imperial camp. Ay, truly
this is the court, yet it takes on the semblance of war
now that we journey behind the true army."

Both of them salaamed abjectly, when, behind a chanting cavalcade of the Sayyids of Barha, Jahangir's elephants paced through the gate—Jahangir himself visible only for a moment when the setting sun struck the diamonds in his aigrette.

"Eh, what splendor!" cried Nasiri. But he was looking at what followed.

Six-foot negro staff-bearers had cleared the avenue, and four riderless elephants loomed behind them, two abreast. In the center of the four walked one giant beast housed in cloth-of-gold. On its back gleamed a dome-shaped howdah of enameled gold. Shutters hid the occupant of the *pitambar* from sight, while permitting her to see out. When the elephant passed under the gate—the top of the dome barely clearing the arch—the men near it turned away or prostrated themselves.

Close to the great golden beast rode a score of women slaves, veiled and armed with scimitar and shield. Behind them a cavalcade of eunuchs in high fringed headdress and shawls. Then the palanquins and horse litters of women attendants, and the concourse of their slaves. A regiment of Pathan horsemen brought up the rear.

"Her Highness Nur Mahal hath a taste for luxury," Farrash whispered, struck by the display.

Then he started violently. The ground quivered under his feet, and irregular thunder beat upon his ears. All the cannon ranged before the gate had been fired, at a signal from the Lord Thunder Thrower. The horses of the Rajput guards reared violently, and screams mingled with shouts of delight from the distant crowd. Smoke swirled back upon the avenue.

For the moment Farrash had forgotten the customary cannon salvo to greet the emperor when he set foot on the ground before his pavilion. It seemed to him that the cannon had been fired too soon—at the instant when Nur Mahal's last followers cleared the gate.

"Who gave command to loose the guns?" he demanded.

"Asaf Khan, our fat and sagacious Master of the Household," replied Nasiri. "I saw him sign to the Turk. And why not?"

"It gave us a taste of battle smoke," Farrash murmured. "But it had the seeming of a salute to Her Highness rather than our lord."

"And why not?" Nasiri laughed.

"Look for an omen before you set out on a journey," the cup companion observed and turned away. Farrash was always on the watch for signs that might mark the way to greater favor, and just now he thought he had seen one. In the quiet of his tent, while his servants stripped him and rubbed him before dressing him in the musk-scented court garments, he pondered it.

He needed a patron. He was, of course, Jahangir's intimate companion over the wine cups. Yet Jahangir sober was not Jahangir drunk, and the poet had seen the tongue torn out of a man who ventured to remind the emperor of a wine-inspired antic. Surely he, Farrash, needed a protector, a voice to speak for him at the Throne.

CONTEMPORARY PAINTING OF
A HAREM SCENE

ASAF KHAN, BROTHER OF NUR MAHAL

FROM "MINIATURE PAINTING OF PERSIA, INDIA AND TURKEY," BY F. R. MARTIN

Wisely, he had taken his time in selecting one. He had considered the war lords, and rejected them; the Rajput princes—it seemed to him that every Rajput noble was a prince—were too unstable, and much too proud to be interested in the career of a versifier. Farrash would have liked one of the treasurers, who had their fingers on the purse strings. But Shaikh Farid—Lord of the Pen and the Sword—was righteous as the Koran itself. He watched every *dinar* and kept nothing for himself.

"Water would not run out of his hand," Farrash muttered.

Ghias Beg, the other money master, was Nur Mahal's father—courteous and painstaking almost beyond belief, and a shrewd administrator. He would accept profitable bribes, but he was old and harassed by the cares of the empire.

"He might take my presents and then hop into his grave."

Nur Mahal, the favorite, and Prince Kurram, the heir, were the two rising stars of India's firmament, and Farrash yearned for some tie, however slight, to bind him to them. And now, in this very hour of sunset, he had perceived such a tie. He had never thought before of his jovial companion Asaf Khan, Master of the Household. Yet Asaf Khan would be his protector.

Sagacious as a fox, a lover of good eating and good fortune, Asaf Khan would have use for a poet. He knew how to make wealth stick to his stout hands, and how to bestow it where it would aid him most. Asaf Khan had just been promoted to the rank of two thousand horse. And Asaf Khan was—Farrash smiled contentedly—the brother of Nur Mahal, the son of Ghias Beg, the father-in-law of Prince Kurram.

"Bring the locked jewel case," he ordered his servants. And from the brassbound casket he selected a splendid black pearl prisoned in a goldwork cage. Wrapping it in silk, he scrawled a verse on scented paper and ordered a servant to take gift and message to the pavilion of the Master of the Household.

After the evening prayer he made his way to the house of the Bath, where groups of nobles were assembling for the evening audience. Farrash had the ability to slip through a crowd—even a crowd jealous of every inch that separated them from the outer gate, or the midway silver railing, or the barrier about the Throne—without drawing a quarrel upon his head. In time he arrived within touch of Asaf Khan, who had posted himself at the steps leading to Jahangir's dais. The restless eyes of the Khan, set in a jovial moon-face, noticed him in a moment, although Farrash gave no sign of his presence. Asaf Khan edged nearer and turned his head to whisper, "Honored am I by the verse of the most favored of poets."

He did not mention the pearl, but Farrash knew that the compliment was the fruit of the pearl, not the poem.

"A poor scrawl," he responded with the semblance of a salaam, "by the hand of an unworthy servant, who desires no more than to place himself in the light of a fortunate star."

"Why—fortunate?"

Farrash smiled discreetly. "Am I one to know the way of the planets? Nay, but I can read omens, and I know the way of fortune."

"Then, O singer of songs, forget not to ask some gift in return."

It was Asaf Khan's way of accepting Farrash's service, tentatively. The two men understood each other perfectly.

For a moment Farrash listened to the talk about the Throne, taking pains to catch Jahangir's eye. The discussion, however, was of revenues and the cost of the army, which did not interest the poet once the Mogul had noticed he was in attendance. Cautiously Farrash edged back until he was behind the lights, then wandered away from the house of the Bath.

Avoiding cresset bearers and keeping out of the range of the Sky Lamp—the great oil beacon raised on a hundred-foot pole to guide late comers to the *lashgar*—he moved nearer the curtain barrier about the quarters of Nur Mahal. The favorite, he knew, would be in the screened space behind Jahangir, who had developed a liking for her company during an audience. But he had reason to think that one of her maids would be elsewhere.

At the barrier entrance he told the guards that he had a message for the head eunuch from Asaf Khan, and as the poet was a privileged person, he was allowed to wander toward the closed pavilions. When he was beyond sight of the guards he slipped into the dark space between the rear wall of Nur Mahal's pavilion and the outer barrier.

"O Sum of Loveliness," he whispered to the shape visible there, "I have a new song to sing to one within. And here is a gift to adorn thee."

A subdued giggle answered him, and the Afghan slave woman who had been posted in the rear of the tent moved a pace or two into the light, peering at a turquoise anklet he had dropped into her hand. It was not the first time Farrash had enlivened her evening of guard duty. The poet, however, sought another woman.

Lying on the ground, invisible in the gloom, he moved along cautiously until he could perceive the glow of a candle through the heavy muslin. After a moment he heard a light chime of silver bracelets, and he tapped gently against the cloth. Silence. Then a half suppressed yawn.

"*Vai*—how dull are these hours!" A soft voice complained within the tent to emptiness.

"How great is this torment," Farrash sighed, "that brings me to thee."

A stir within. "But why come?" the girl's voice wondered, and Farrash knew she must be alone.

"Is it not natural," he quoted shamelessly a rival's verse, "for the lover to die at the threshold of the beloved? Nay, how could he live elsewhere? He has come, that the swords of the guards may drink his blood!"

(The Afghan woman crept closer, fearful of missing a word of this magnificent exhortation, and a distinct sigh from within the pavilion rewarded Farrash.)

"And who is he?"

"Farrash, the singer of songs, who pours into the dull ears of India a music unknown until now. And what is this music but the echo of thy voice?"

A gentle laugh, then expectant silence. Love-making demanded strong compliments, and the poet drew upon a wide experience, until even the Afghan woman gasped and bethought her to watch lest anyone come within hearing. But the invisible girl seemed content.

". . . and the rising sun," he ended, "will find me lifeless upon the ground, if she will not grant me sight of her face and touch of her hand."

"There is a tear in this seam that ought to be mended."

Anxiously the poet investigated the nearest seam and discovered where the threads had been cut. With his dagger he enlarged the tear promptly, and peered in—remembering to catch his breath as he did so. Maryam was curled up among cushions a yard away outwardly demure and unconscious of his scrutiny. She was veiled to the eyes, but a spider's web had more substance than that veil of gossamer, and Farrash exclaimed brokenly upon the beauty of a mouth like the seal of Solomon, hair blacker than the storm wind, and a body like a young willow swaying in the wind. "Yet the eyes are hidden."

Swiftly she glanced up at the dark slit, and away.

"A gazelle looked at me," he whispered, and begged her to extinguish the candle before his senses left him.

When she did so there was silence for so long that the Afghan began to be fearful, and came nearer, relieved that the poet was only kissing the girl's face, through the aperture.

"Get ye gone, O shameless one, mocker of women!" she whispered warning. "It is time *she* came from the Throne."

With real reluctance Farrash tore himself away, pressing to his lips a silk bangle he had taken from Maryam's wrist. This girl was almost innocent, he thought—nothing over eight years of course could be wholly innocent within the curtains of the Mogul's court. Otherwise her fingers would not have trembled so, and she would not have cried when she was caressed. What luck, for him! If he could make her infatuation complete he would have the eyes and ears of Nur Mahal's confidential maid to serve him. It was best, always, to have two strings to a bow, and he would have Asaf Khan to beg from and Maryam to command. Besides, the intrigue would be pleasant, it seemed.

He was smiling as he left the pavilion, deep in thought. Yet he noticed a white figure that moved without sound over the grass. An instant he stared, and caught his breath without any pretense. Bending his head swiftly he raised both hands to his forehead.

"What seekest thou, O maker of verses?"

How could he have known that Nur Mahal would return alone, unlighted except by the distant Sky Lamp that outlined her slimness, wrapped from head to foot in sheer white silk?

"I came—I came—" he blundered, and decided upon flattery—"to bring to the Light of the Palace a poor verse of my own."

"And what is it?"

What could it be? Farrash groped desperately into memory, and bethought him of the now notorious tiger hunt. That, at least, would be safe, and would please Jahangir.

"*The eyes of Nur Mahal,*" he improvised, "*slay men as her hand overthrows a tiger.*"

But he was aware that the dark eyes behind the silk flashed dangerously, and then he recalled the name of her first husband, killed by Jahangir's unintentional command. Farrash was bold enough; still, in that instant he saw himself blinded and dragged before an elephant, to be trodden. Why had he not remembered Shir Afgan, the Tiger Thrower, in time?

The white figure did not move, or breathe more quickly. It seemed to contemplate him curiously.

"Either you are more stupid," she said, "or you are much bolder than you look just now. I do not think I care to listen to more of your love-making behind a curtain."

For once in his life Farrash became tongue-tied. Had she been listening a moment ago? Had she eyes, as some said, that could see in the dark? Was she playing with him, or only a little amused?

"Highness," he blundered, bending lower to hide his face, "may—may Heaven preserve Your Highness. Will she forgive——"

He did not hear Nur Mahal go, but she was gone, into the canopied pavilion entrance, leaving a faint scent of warm roses in the dusty air. Farrash straight-

ened slowly and felt perspiration drip into his eyes.
As he wiped it away mechanically, walking through
the barrier gate, he heard a deep voice at his ear.

"I think this one is a fool."

"Ay, Ahmed," responded another, "because he is
certainly no bolder than he looks."

With a snarl the poet peered to right and left, at
two tall Pathan troopers lounging at the gate. When
he put his hand on his knife hilt, they grasped their
sabers, their teeth flashing exultingly in the mesh of
their black beards. Farrash knew better than to draw
steel before these men. He spat, and walked away in
a fever of rage.

"He is brave enough," one of the troopers flung
after him, "with words. Not with deeds."

In a bad temper Farrash sought his own quarters
and abused the slaves who hastened to bring him
wine and undress him. What possessed the woman,
to walk in the night? No wonder she could influence
Jahangir.

"She could even move Prince Kurram," he
thought. "Unless they became enemies."

This gave him food for contemplation, so that he
lay awake far into the night, forgetting to punish his
slaves.

Jahangir felt the heat of the south, into which they
were moving. That night his broad face was lined
and pale, with circles of exhaustion under the eyes.
He carried himself erect as always, but his limbs
felt moist and flabby, and he was athirst for his eve-

ning opium when he entered Nur Mahal's pavilion as usual before going to his sleeping quarters.

It surprised him to find the pavilion altered—the carpets seemed to be masses of flowers, and surely flowers had been ranged by the walls, which were hung with silk tapestries embroidered in designs of gardens with people outlined in gold thread. So cleverly had it been done that the human beings appeared to stand out from the cool backgrounds, and the deception was heightened by a breath of outer air from unseen fans revolving beneath the upper canopy.

Lights had been hidden behind the flowers, and an opening somewhere admitted the silvery glow of the Sky Lamp, giving the illusion of moonlight. Running water trickled down the runways of alabaster fountains.

And Nur Mahal herself seemed changed. She had been bathed and anointed with sandalwood oil and showed no least sign of the haste in which she had made ready for him. Her dark hair was caught within a silver head-net, and she wore only the thin sheet wrapped about her waist and drawn over her shoulders after the bath.

Jahangir had meant to exchange a word with her and to go on to Prithvi's encampment for the opium which would bring him sleep. The Persian, however, seemed to have nothing to say. She sat idly by one of the fountains, chin on hand, as if oblivious of the empire and its master. Jahangir, lying beside her, wondered at the still, intent face that would flash into

a brilliant smile, or turn to him with childish eagerness at a word. Yet his whole body craved the first
relaxation of the opium draft.

"Why is it," he murmured, "I must go elsewhere
for that?"

She must have followed his thoughts, because she
answered at once.

"I am jealous of my lord's love."

"Thou?" He smiled. "And why?"

"The drug takes him from me. I would like him
to have only one need and one vice."

"I have many. But what is the one?"

Bending swiftly, her eyes looked into his, and her
lips brushed his mouth. Jahangir felt as if a statue
had come to life and movement for a second, and
he found the experience pleasant. He did not know
that Nur Mahal was deeply disappointed that he
had not been more delighted with the moonlight
scene she had arranged with great pains, and being
disappointed, felt determined to keep him from the
lure of Prithvi and opium that night. She did not
know how she would do so.

Jahangir had other thoughts. "For three years
thou hast been wife of mine, and yet I know thee
not."

"How should you? I am not of the palace." The
smooth brow puckered. "I have known need and had
bitterness to eat. Even when I waited for word of
war or misfortune, I worked with my hands. My
people are the common ones of the world. I still
carry a cotton doll with me." She nodded content-

edly. "Its face is worn off, but I do not want to paint a new one."

This sudden change of mood was beyond Jahangir's plodding thought. Except for the sallies into the hunting field, he had never been outside the attendance of the court, nor did it seem possible for him now to be so. He tried to imagine what his wife's girlhood had been, and gave up the task as too arduous. The steady drip-drip of the fountain drew his mind.

"Thou hast adorned my court with new splendor." Drip-splash, drip-splash. He closed his eyes. "But, Mihri of mine, never did I know a woman who did not want new dolls to play with."

Her fingertips caressed his eyelids. "Yet mine is an old doll and quite ruined."

"What would you like, to play with?"

"Oh, many things." While the fountain dripped, her low voice soothed him, telling of a fantastic journey they would make after the war, to the hills where the snow peaks stood against the sky.

"Ay, Kashmir," he murmured drowsily. "Strange birds are there, for the hawks."

Then he slept, and she sat without moving, not to disturb him. Late she watched the drip of the water, and Prithvi waited in vain for his coming.

After daybreak, when Jahangir had gone out to the first prayer, Nur Mahal called for Maryam. A maid came, saying that the orphan girl was not in any compartment of the pavilion, and a search through the outer tents found her missing.

Nur Mahal called in the chief of the eunuchs, who questioned the Afghan slaves savagely, without result. Nor would the outer guards admit that any woman had gone forth. Maryam had been in the pavilion before her mistress's return; after that no one had seen her. The tigerskin on which she had slept was rumpled and drawn half across her nook of the sleeping compartment, but the bags that held her trinkets and perfumes had not been touched.

Certainly Maryam would not have crept away in the darkness without her treasures, and Nur Mahal knew that the girl would not willingly have left the quarters. But she had vanished.

Until the drums sounded and Jahangir mounted for the day's march, Nur Mahal would not give up the search for her maid. In the confusion of fifty thousand souls preparing for the road not a trace of the orphan girl could be found.

That evening, when they had reached the new camp—a double set of the Mogul's pavilions enabled them to occupy fresh quarters in readiness each day —Maryam returned. As the bearers filed into the enclosure with the maids' palanquins, and the girls slid out, stretching their cramped limbs, they noticed that the screens of one palanquin remained shut.

A slave opened the side and peered in, then fell upon her knees, wailing. On the cushions Maryam lay dead. Her cheeks had been made up and her hair dressed, yet the lifeless eyes had not been closed. In the stiffened fingers a roll of paper lay.

It was brought to Nur Mahal, who read it in silence. *"Let the one who walks in the nights take heed to her steps. For the high, as well as the low, a grave is dug."*

The writing was Persian, in a firm, minute hand unknown to her. She hardly listened when the palanquin guards came and stammered how Maryam's body had been brought in by two strange palanquin bearers, who had appeared just as the lashgar entered the camp. They had attracted no attention in the confusion of the arrival, and had slipped away as soon as their burden was set down by the pavilion. They had looked like Mahrattas—others said Afghans—but they had vanished among thousands of their kind, and to search for them would be like looking for two grains of sand in the dry desert. Nor did it surprise her when the women who had examined the girl's body said that Maryam must have died of poisoning, since there was no wound mark upon the skin. The murderers had even embalmed the body.

"Let nothing be said outside my household," Nur Mahal commanded.

For a moment she went to look at the slain girl, then withdrew to her sleeping room. She read the paper scroll again, curiously, seeking for the message between the lines. A threat, of course, but also a hint that someone knew she had broken pardah. Someone who had wrung information from Maryam, perhaps, before killing the girl.

Prithvi might have done it—being more merciless than the tame leopard of the harem. Yet Nur Mahal did not think that it would satisfy Prithvi to slay a maid and send such a crude written warning. Farrash, who had been singing his love to Maryam, might have enticed her away from the guards, but he would never have sent back her body. For the rest, the Persian knew she had made no particular enemies. She had never sided in the quarrels of the harem, and who would dare strike a blow at the reigning favorite?

In the mass of human beings that pressed around the jeweled throne of the emperor, someone had snatched the girl from her, and had sent her this warning for a reason that would be revealed later. Nur Mahal knew that it would be, and when that time came she meant to take vengeance for Maryam.

She had lost one of the three living things she loved. Lardili, her daughter, hidden safely in the suburb of Agra, could not be harmed because, except herself and the child's nurse and Arslan, no one knew the hiding place. And Jahangir was the shadow of God in this land—only one of his own sons would venture to make an attempt upon his life. And his sons had no reason to turn against him—it would be only folly to try their strength against the Padishah.

For she loved Jahangir. She had loved him when she was fourteen and had watched from behind the lattices for his coming into the harem garden—when he had been a sulky boy cutting at flowers with his stick. She did not think of him now as the Padishah; he was the same cruel and good-natured boy, looking from wearied eyes for something new to amuse him. He was part of her, with his heavy, troubled breathing and the indolent body that belonged to her. . . .

She was lying on her couch with the stained cot-

ton doll in her hands when they came to dress her
that night in readiness for Jahangir's visit.

The lashgar climbed steadily to long grass plains,
where villages were few and the night air grew cooler. It halted beneath the wall of a city overlooking
lakes and a range that marked the beginning of the
Rajput lands.

Here, at Ajmere, it remained. Jahangir betook
him to the hunting in the foothills, while he waited
for news of the campaign against the Rana of
Mewar. Prince Kurram departed with the army, and
a veteran general to assist him. He was fortunate, or
the Rajputs—whose cousins served against them in
the Mogul's host—had been disheartened by previous campaigns. So fortunate that the aged general
was recalled, to allow Kurram to take full credit for
success.

Outwardly, he achieved a triumph. Word came to
the lashgar at Ajmere of victories gained, and of
Kurram's sagacity in persuading the hard-pressed
Rana, whose ancestors had never bowed head to conqueror, to submit to the Mogul. True, the head of
the Rajputs need not appear in person to render submission; but he sent his son, whom Jahangir overwhelmed with gifts. He even ordered two stone
statues of Rajput Ranas to be made and placed outside the jharoka window in Agra. And he rewarded
Kurram with such eager abandon that the aged
general was forgotten, and the court turned into a
continuous *darbar*.

Nur Mahal added her gifts to the emperor's,

presenting the wild Rajput prince with a jeweled sword and a magnificent elephant. She was occupied hourly with the planning of new feasts, and the poets sang that the lashgar had been transformed to a vision of fairyland.

Then came rumors from the north. Plague had appeared in the hill villages. It was felt in Lahore. Tales were told of death fires seen burning in the sky at night. On certain houses of Agra circles were found drawn in white chalk one morning.

Scientists who accompanied the court explained to Jahangir that the last two years had been dry, and the lack of rain brought sickness from the water. Astrologers mentioned a comet seen in the north, and the court wasted little thought upon the new sickness that killed victims in a day—until word came down the caravan road that the plague had entered Agra.

A groom from the *caravanserai* brought the word to Nur Mahal's outer guard, who told the Afghans, who hastened to her with the tidings. Within a half hour she was standing before Jahangir, her eyes wide with anxiety.

"Shaikhu Baba, give me leave to go from thy presence for half a moon."

"And wherefore?" He scented some new frolic. "Would the Light desert the Palace."

"Ay, so—if it please my lord—now, at once."

"What madness is this?"

She had been too impetuous, forgetting that Jahangir could never be hurried. So she knelt by him, her face growing luminous as she pleaded to be allowed to ride to Agra. Lardili, her daughter, was under the care of a single nurse in the plague-stricken city. They must be found—perhaps they had tried to leave already—and brought to safety. She would take her Pathan guardsmen and the eunuch Ambar and go at once.

"To the sickness?" Jahangir smiled indulgently. "That may not be."

He would send dispatch riders, instead, with a message to the people of the Agra citadel, who would search for the child. It had been madness enough for Nur Mahal to leave the harem once, disguised.

"Shaikhu Baba!" She checked the torrent of her words. How could she explain that the palace people would not know Lardili or the nurse, and that they would think first of their own health? They could not care for the child—she thought of Maryam's body. She had been in a plague city before, and knew what the outpouring of people into the country would be. "Better would it be for me to send the message."

"May God shield thy daughter." Jahangir was sentimental about children.

Nur Mahal kissed his hand—a thing she rarely did—and he granted her forgiveness when she begged for it wistfully. Then she withdrew.

When he went to her enclosure that night after the last audience he was a little surprised by the deep prostration of her women. One of them offered him a silk bracelet with cheap bangles on it. With a start he recognized the one that had been sent him in the Agra citadel when Nur Mahal confessed that she had left the harem.

But by then she was four hours' ride away, in the garments of Khalil Khan, with Arslan galloping at her side.

At midnight they were cantering down toward the plains. In the clear starlight camel-thorn showed dark against the sand. The cool wind of the height no longer caressed them, and the horses became damp with sweat. Already they had left one of the lashgar's camp sites behind them, when Arslan pointed out the white wall of a caravanserai.

They let the horses turn in, under the arched entrance, and Nur Mahal stood by the glow of a dung fire while the old Turk roused the keeper of the place and demanded fresh beasts. The keeper was an Afghan, and suspicious of two who rode at such a pace.

"He says our mounts were stolen from the emperor's stable," Arslan explained in a whisper. "And he will give us nothing."

"I have jewels. Let him take some."

"Wallahi! If he saw a jewel, he would want to rob us. Wait here, my lady, and I will deal with him."

Arslan disappeared into the darkness, and presently Nur Mahal heard the thumping of blows delivered by a sheathed sword on a man's body, followed by angry grunts and a placating whine. Horses stamped restlessly, and sleepers roused on the gallery above them to fling angry questions down into the yard. But the serai keeper preserved a discreet silence after his beating—Arslan had arms like a bear—and two fresh mounts were led out. Muttering to himself, the big Turk changed saddles, putting Nur Mahal's upon the better horse, a lean gray Arab.

"Blows are good," he observed as they mounted and found the road again. "It is bad to offer money to dogs like that."

In the darkness he had lost his awe of the woman. The starlight showed him no more than the slender figure of an ahadi, a gentleman trooper, and he heard only the low voice of the girl Mihri. A ride like this did not tax his iron limbs, but after an hour his knees began to ache, and it occurred to him that his companion must be suffering.

"Eh," he suggested, "let us stop and breathe the horses. Then my lady can rest. It is far to Agra's walls."

"How far—how long to ride?"

Rubbing his beard, Arslan pondered and counted on the fingers of his free hand. "We have come fast, down from the hills. We have passed Sambhar. An imperial courier would ride from here without rest and reach Agra's gate in the time between one sunrise and the next. Nay, my lady could not do that. Perhaps, insha'allah, we shall dismount at Agra after another day and a night and two watches of the following day."

"So long!" Nur Mahal pulled in the gray Arab to let him breathe. In spite of the soft quilt Arslan had placed on her high peaked saddle and the heavy

leather breeches she had put on over silk, her back
ached continuously, and the soft skin on the inside of
her thighs smarted from the saddle chafing. She did
not feel hungry or especially tired, but the pain was
taking its toll of her. For long years she had not sat a
saddle through the night. "I do not wish to rest
here. Perhaps at noon we will eat, and I can sleep a
little. Now I will stop for a while—hold thou the
horses."

It was a deserted stretch of road, screened by thorn
bush and overlooked by the skeleton of a ruined
watchtower above the dry bed of a stream. Nur
Mahal dismounted, aided by Arslan, and left him,
to walk a few paces among the outflung arms of
thorn. Undoing her turban end, she tore off a couple
of yards of the white silk—using her teeth as well
as her fingers. Tearing this in half again, she bound
the strips around her thighs above the knees, after
rubbing the tortured skin with oil from a silver flask
she had brought, remembering other rides.

Adjusting her girdle cloth, and knotting up the
diminished turban, she was returning to the horses
when she heard Arslan call urgently. From the road
behind them sounded a beat of hoofs, drawing nearer
swiftly. As she reached the road, a flaring torch came
over the rise by the ruined tower.

Three men—a gaunt bearded Rajput, a servant,
and a lance-bearer—reined in at sight of them, and
her heart quickened at the thought that these might
be the advance of pursuers. Arslan, however, had
noticed the wallet strapped to the Rajput's chest, and

stamped with the imperial *tamgha*. "A good road to the post rider!" he laughed.

Suspiciously the Rajput peered about him, for thieves were common on the caravan road, and he carried the emperor's dispatch. "What men are ye?" he growled.

"Khalil Khan, lord of Iran, and his serv——"

"Whose men be ye, who ride at the star setting without a light?"

Nur Mahal made answer quickly. "We be followers of the Sirdar, Mahabat Khan, who hath summoned us to the north. Truly we be weary of this fever-ridden land, and we go in haste to obey our lord. Mahabat Khan hath no love for laggards."

His brow clearing, the courier nodded. The great general was well liked by the hard-fighting Rajputs, and Nur Mahal's words were candor itself.

With a muttered "Swashti!" and a cry to his followers, the dispatch rider clapped his heels into his horse and was off across the gully, vanishing down the road with a jingling of bells. For a moment their two horses galloped in an effort to keep pace with the fast disappearing riders, but Arslan reined in to the easy lope that covers distance with the least effort.

"Those yonder," he explained, "bestride racing beasts and spare them not. Ours are better fitted for carts."

His own mount was going lame, stumbling against hidden stones. Nur Mahal was wondering what message the courier carried to Agra, and whether Jahangir had actually sent pursuit after them. If so, they would soon be caught up, unless Arslan could find another mount. In this part of the road with only huddles of peasants' huts in the fields, there was no prospect of fresh horses. Impatiently she held back her Arab to avoid leaving Arslan behind, until his pony stumbled heavily and came up sweating.

"By Allah," the Turk swore, "he would not keep pace with a plow."

Under his lashing the pony trotted a while, then limped to a walk.

"Arslan," she cried, "I cannot wait. Seek thou another horse after the coming of day, and follow."

Urging on the gray horse, she was out of reach before the old servant grasped her purpose. Then he wailed aloud.

"*Ai,* my lady! Will you lay shame upon my head? Only God knows the peril of the road for thee. Wait, I will run beside thee——"

His voice died away, leaving silence and the creaking of the leather beneath her. At times the Arab tossed his head, with a clatter of bit against teeth. Nur Mahal stroked his neck and leaned forward to rub him behind the ears. True, he was a little beast, but he went on nicely. Being a pacer, and sure-footed as all his race, his gait was much easier for her than that of the first horse.

For a while the road was a gray patch before her, and she paid little heed to it, knowing that the pony would choose his way without guidance. Once he tossed his head and turned his ears toward the dark mass of a caravan quartered for the night among its bales. Nur Mahal sniffed camels and stale smoke, and heard a watchman cough and spit as she passed. Then the road became lighter, and she could see the outlines of trees against the pale sky ahead of her.

In a moment, so it seemed, the fire of the sun struck her tired eyes, and a fresh wind sent dust swirling by her. Curiously she looked around. Never since her childhood had she seen the sunrise outside the women's quarters. It was as if she had come out naked into a strange world where smoke eddied up from the roof holes of thatch huts, and strings of laden camels appeared at the edge of the road. A boy, throwing stones after a herd of black goats, turned to stare at her. The caravan road was resuming its daily life.

At a whitewashed house in a poplar grove she stopped to let the Arab breathe and drink a little before the heat of the day. A pock-marked peasant emerged fearfully from a thorn fence to inquire the pleasure of the great lord.

"A bowl of milk, if I may have it," she responded gratefully.

The man, who had expected a cursing and a demand for fodder from a dust-coated ahadi, hastened to bring warm milk, while naked children clustered at a respectful distance from the horse. Nur Mahal sipped at the bowl, amused at the sight of her stained, reddened hands from which she had stripped all the rings.

"Eh!" exclaimed the peasant. "The noble lord hath the hands of a young girl, so soft and dainty." He gazed at his own claws, into which dirt had caked. When the bowl was returned to him he started, unbelieving. A gold *muhr* lay within it.

Bewildered, he shouted after the ahadi, who was turning back to the road. "The noble lord hath made a mistake. Here is gold, not black money nor white, but *gold*."

"Then give the praise to Allah," Nur Mahal called over her shoulder. And the man stood in the sunlight, astounded at this rider who gave gold knowingly and laughed like an *houri* from Paradise.

As the morning wore on, the houri from Paradise began to be thoroughly weary. The sun beat upon her shoulders, and the dust stung her drowsy eyes that closed involuntarily whenever the pony dropped into a walk. The road itself had become a lane of noise and dust.

Strings of laden camels bound for Ajmere stalked past bullock carts that creaked through the ruts. Knots of villagers gathered wherever there was shade, to watch the cavalcades of horsemen going up to the Mogul's court. And Nur Mahal had to turn out more and more frequently.

At noon she felt the need of rest. She dismounted and let the pony drink at a stone tank in front of a shrine. When he had finished she led him into the deep shade of a plantain grove, waving away impatiently a pair of gaunt dervishes who came up to beg. This was no place to reveal that she carried gold upon her, and she had brought no other money. Pulling the gray pony after her, she climbed around the plantain roots, pushed through the grass of an open glade—starting fearfully as some animal scurried away underfoot—and reached the shelter of heavy brush.

Here she tied the grazing rope, which Arslan had placed on the saddle, to the loosened headstall, letting the pony feed as best he could. She even managed to get the saddle off, whereupon he rolled at once luxuriously in the dry grass. Lying down beside him, she listened to the clatter from the road and to strange stirrings in the brush, until drowsiness overcame dread, and she slept heavily.

It was late afternoon when she woke and found the pony snuffling over her head.

"Rafik," she smiled up at him. "My companion of the road—was ever a guarded woman in such a place before?"

Rafik blew forcibly, and she stood up, stretching her stiffened limbs. "May it please God," she thought, "that he does not make himself big when I put on the saddle."

She was just able to lift the saddle and set it on his back. If the pony had swelled himself out when she tightened the girth, she could never have adjusted it. But the pony only nipped playfully at her arm when she drew it tight with all the strength of her slender shoulders, and he allowed her to slip the bit back between his teeth.

"Shabash," she whispered, rubbing his ears. "Take care not to stumble, because I cannot ride as once I could. But go swiftly, swiftly."

With the sun at his back and the level plain stretching endlessly before him, the gray pony settled down to a steady pace that ate up the leagues, until the day wind died and dusk hid the hollows. The red eyes of fires winked along the road, which had become empty, magically. Nur Mahal, who had looked in vain for a sign of Arslan, dismounted finally by a group of Hindu disciples with the ash mark of Ram on their foreheads. These, at least, she thought, would not be quarrelsome.

Although they looked astonished when a slender gentleman trooper, who was undoubtedly a Persian, asked for food, they shared with Nur Mahal their buttered *kichri* and fruit—she sitting apart to eat in such silence that they wondered anew. In spite of her passionate longing to speed to Agra and her strange sense of freedom among these wandering human beings, Nur Mahal could not free herself from the habits of the veiled women. It was hard for her to sit down and eat where men, even disciples of the temple, could see her.

Someone else had been observing her, for a stout man with one blind white eye crossed the road, chewing a strip of fried mutton. He spat toward the Hindus, circled the gray pony, and came to a stand by Nur Mahal. The fringe of his shawl girdle was dark with grease, and he reeked of garlic and mutton. Presently he wiped his hands on his hips.

"Will your honor," he asked, "buy a horse? A better one than this lame nag with a cracked hoof?"

She shook her head, putting away the rest of her supper—having lost her appetite at his coming.

"I have aspan-dawandi—good horses," he persisted. "They can win races, and you can sell them

for more in Agra. By the eyes of the Prophet, horses
are being bought in that city to carry people away.
Will your honor come to see my lot?"

Again she refused. The stout horse trader was only
a ride from Agra himself; why should he sell horses
on the road, so near to higher prices?

"Have you no tongue?" he demanded, dropping
the mask of courtesy. "Does a true ahadi sit thus in
the grass without servant or wine? This horse hath
not the brand of an ahadi upon him. What manner
of youth art thou?" He leaned closer, his bleared
eyes intent. *"Hai,* thou art a girl, in man's dress. Give
me gold, and I will say naught of it."

She wanted to shrink away from him and offer
him all the muhrs in her wallet before he should
touch her. But it would not do to show fear.

"May dogs litter on thy grave!" she cried hoarsely,
springing to her feet. "May thy face be blackened
and thy beard pulled apart! Have the women in thy
land no noses, that thou shouldst mistake me for
one?"

Bewildered by the swift abuse, the horse trader
fell back a pace, and before he could think of a new
trick, Nur Mahal glanced casually across the road,
going to the stirrup of the gray pony. "I may buy
one of your nags. Hold my stirrup!"

It was as natural for a gentleman trooper to mount
his horse to go fifty paces as to command a lesser person to assist him to mount—or to know why women
in the Panjab had their noses cut off. The dealer hastened to obey; then, noticing how Nur Mahal sat in

the saddle, fresh suspicion stirred in him, and he caught at the rein. Before his hand reached it, she turned the pony aside and made off down the road.

"Um Kulsum! Daughter of sin!" the man howled after her. "Witch in breeches! Mother of deceit— may jackals dig thy grave."

He contented himself with shouting, having in reality no horses to sell or to ride, as she had more than suspected. But she heard a hoofbeat behind her and saw a small pony galloping up. Its rider flapped his arms and thumped about the saddle as if unaccustomed to such a pace, and when he reached her side he reined in with a sigh of relief.

"Oh, but I would not be a trooper such as you! Now, tell me, what talk was this of a woman?"

Nur Mahal thought despairingly that this road was never without eyes and ears. Fortunately in the deep twilight the newcomer could barely see her, and he looked like a harmless musician. From beneath his cloak the bulbed end of a vina projected, and he carried no weapons.

"That thieving dog," she exclaimed, "tried to steal my wallet but could not."

The player nodded understanding. He kept jerking his head from side to side, and his small bright eyes looked like a ferret's.

"There is so much evil, so little mercy," he sighed. "Now this very morning I heard a grave bird croak as I set out. What an unfortunate omen, as I turned my face to Agra, where they are carrying the black bodies of the plague-slain to the river. By the right hand of Siva, I wish that my road led elsewhere."

"Are many dying?" she asked involuntarily.

"So many that they drop down in the mosques of the Moslems. It is said that the plague is born of rats, which infect cats, and so the dread thing—the gods have never before sent such a punishment— passes into human beings, and all die alike, the strong and the lovely among the first. They grow dark in the face, then they begin to vomit blood, and finally the flux——"

"Be silent!" she cried.

"The only cure is for a householder to offer to a temple a gold cow of four tolahs weight, having silver horns and a copper hump, and a brass vessel for its milk—besides eating only curds, butter, and cow dung. That is also the cure for dumbness, which affliction comes by favor of the gods as punishment for killing a sister. Meanwhile, touch nothing from the house of a courtesan or dancer or dog keeper or wine seller or surgeon or eunuch. But I forget, thou art of the Moslems, and so there is no cure for thee."

"In what part of Agra is the sickness?"

"By the river, they say. Surely the sins of the reigning city have been great, that such a visitation should come." The Hindu sighed profoundly. "First, in the court arose the sin of lobha, which is overweening desire of wealth and display. Second, raga, which is lust for pleasures of the flesh. Third and greatest of all was the sin of mada which is intoxication from wine or pride. Now have the gods sent punishment, and the haughty Moslems die like flies in the serais."

"Thou art a true grave bird, with thy croaking."

Angrily she lashed the gray pony with the rein end and cantered ahead of the prophet of misfortune.

"Stay—I will give thee a charm to ward off the sickness."

But she went on, into the night, oblivious of everything except the need to reach Lardili in Agra. Once, when she paused to rest the stolid little horse, she thought—the last hours had sharpened her ears for such sounds—she heard someone on the road behind her. And instinct told her that the Hindu musician had been more dangerous than the stout robber.

Rafik lagged, and Nur Mahal drowsed from very weariness as the sun came up again, striking upon a red ridge beside them. Atop the ridge stood the sandstone ramparts of a half-ruined city, the gilt worn from its domes, and the great artificial lake beside the road half choked with weeds. It was the red city of Akbar's court, built at an emperor's whim, and now deserted. Without entering, Nur Mahal circled the walls and headed down the straight road to Agra.

Now that the ride was almost at an end, she urged on the Arab fiercely and no longer looked behind her. They pressed on through dust and clamor, past the throngs hastening out of Agra. Within sight of the river Rafik stretched out his head and essayed a gallop that carried them through a gate and into the crowded alleys—past the bazaar and down to the wooded suburb by the water. At Ayesha's lime-washed hut she reined in with a deep breath of sheer relief. The door was open, and the nurse's shrill voice echoed within.

Then two horsemen who had been following her through the alleys spurred to either side of her. A third circled in front of her, smiling. With a start of dread she recognized the Hindu musician.

He rode a fresh horse, and there was mockery in his restless eyes as he half salaamed before her.

"Be wise, O Pearl of the Empire, and come with us. I am not to be tricked like the fat robber."

Nur Mahal glanced to right and left. The two men were Mahrattas, ragged and insolent enough. They could not have come from Jahangir, and they bore no mark of other service upon them.

"We waited long for you, my lady," the musician explained, "at the Fathpur gate. Take her rein, Rawut——"

The two Mahrattas, however, turned away from her with a single impulse, drawing their swords and shouting. Out of the orchard by the house Arslan appeared, running with his shield up. Beside him came a tall Pathan, whom Nur Mahal recognized as one of her Agra bodyguard.

In a voiceless rage Arslan flung himself at the nearest rider. He took the slash of a scimitar on his shield and struck savagely with his curved sword. The blade caught the man across the chest, biting through his quilted coat, sending him reeling back against the saddle.

The other horse plunged against Nur Mahal's pony, and she was thrust aside, while dust swirled up, and a man yelled in agony. She saw the Pathan throw a javelin, and heard steel blades grate together.

Then the dust subsided, and she was looking down

at a human body that lifted itself feebly and fell back. The other Mahratta was riding off, swaying in the saddle, and the musician had disappeared.

Arslan wiped his sword on the coat of the dying man and muttered, "The praise to God you are here. What dogs are these?"

She could only shake her head as the Pathan helped her to dismount. Ayesha was screaming for her men folk when Nur Mahal entered, and Lardili ran to greet her.

An hour later an agitated eunuch of Nur Mahal's household, summoned by the Pathan, arrived with a palki and bearers. And for once Nur Mahal was happy to lie behind closed screens, borne swiftly toward the citadel, with Arslan leading the gray pony beside her. Lardili, propped on an elbow, gazed wide-eyed into her mother's face, coated with dust.

"What has happened?" the girl asked.

"Nay," the Persian smiled, "I know not. But I know this, heart of mine—thou wilt not live else-where than at my side."

Tired out in body, Nur Mahal slept most of that day and night, waking to talk with Lardili and watch the ten-year-old girl play with the glittering orna-ments of the sleeping gallery. It seemed to her that she could never see enough of Lardili.

The palace itself was blessedly quiet, most of the people being at Ajmere. Guards at the gates kept the townswomen out, to escape contagion. Only at times in the distance she heard the chanting of Moslems carrying bodies to burial. And down the river smoke rose steadily from the pyres where the Hindus burned their dead.

The next morning the eunuch Ambar arrived from Ajmere, his black face lined with suspense, and his grizzled wool awry. Never before had the faithful Abyssinian had to chase one of his charges on horse-back. He brought with him some of her personal maids and a cavalry guard—sent by Jahangir's order. The emperor had said nothing publicly about her absence, and the other women of the court be-lieved that she had gone to Agra with Ambar.

"And the Padishah?"

"His august attention is still upon the Rana's son. He sleeps much, and hath a new companion, a man from over the black water who wears shoes and a hat with a brim—an Inglisi."[1]

Ambar explained that Jahangir wished the Per-sian to remain at Agra until the crowds fleeing from the city ceased to block the roads. And for days no further word came from him. This troubled the old eunuch, who saw utter disgrace awaiting the fa-vorite, and worse in store for him. When he learned of the fight in front of Ayesha's house, he tore at his hair and fell to praying—then went to the stables to interrogate Arslan.

The old Turk, however, proved noncommittal. This time, he felt himself to be doomed, and what man could alter the fate in store for him? It was all written down in the book of fate.

"By Allah, how could it be otherwise? Yet the

[1]Englishman.

dogs who set upon my lady will lick their wounds a long time."

Nothing more had been seen of the two survivors. Nur Mahal thought that the musician was a spy, perhaps one of many who had been sent to the highway to watch for her. Certainly he had known her, at the door of Ayesha's house, and had meant to make her prisoner. He might have been a servant of the one who slew Maryam. Perhaps, having failed to seize her, he had been quietly strangled by his master—or mistress—to silence his tongue. But who had sent him?

It must have been someone close enough to the harem to know of her setting out for Agra, and someone high enough to profit by the open disgrace of the favorite. And someone adroit enough to find her in disguise among the thousands on the Agra road. She had, it seemed, an enemy wise as herself.

Not long was Nur Mahal left to herself in the Agra harem. In spite of the guards, women flocked to the outer court to send in the tale of their troubles to the Padishahi Begam—the imperial princess, mistress of the harem. There were girls who had lost their parents and had no other sanctuary open to them; there were wives who sought protection from feudal enemies during the rioting and confusion.

One Hindu girl of a higher caste sat impassively in the Queen's Hall until Nur Mahal noticed her and stopped to speak to her. The girl performed no prostration—it would have defiled her in the eyes of her relatives if she had touched the Persian—but her

frightened eyes made mute appeal to the woman
whose beauty set her apart from the others.

Jodh Bai, she called herself, and explained that
she was twelve years of age. Her husband, an older
man of the same warrior caste, had died two days
before of the plague, and his relatives wished her to
burn at his pyre, to honor him. But she was afraid of
the fire—she wept as she told it—and besides, she
loved a young Hindu of a lower caste very much.
He had promised that if she became a widow he
would carry her away with him and make her his
wife. Knowing that she would become outcast from
her own people if she did so, she still longed for her
lover, and that was a great sin. Only, she was afraid
of the flames—not of death, but of the fire that would
blacken her flesh.

"Now," she murmured, *"he* will not send for me
or look at me, because he fears my husband's relatives and the Brahmans."

She had fled from her house, Jodh Bai explained,
to the protection of the imperial princess, from
whose rooms not even the Brahmans would dare remove her. Yet, after they had burned her husband's
body, she would be without honor, being also deserted by the Hindu who had wooed her secretly. All
this had come upon her head because she was a coward.

"Clean and make ready the small room of the
towels," Nur Mahal ordered the maids who were
with her. "And see that lawful food is prepared for
Jodh Bai."

The girl shook her head silently. She could not eat.

"And then," the Persian said softly, "when the burning is past we will talk again. Thou art safe, Jodh Bai."

It was dangerous to interfere with the Brahmans in their burial rite, yet she had seen the worn-out eyes of the child who was no more than the fragile remnant of a human body.

On the second day she remembered Jodh Bai, and sent for her, only to learn that the Hindu girl had left the harem the day before. Some older women, relatives it seemed, had come to talk with her behind closed doors. Jodh Bai had gone away with them without a word to the attendants.

This would have been, Nur Mahal reflected, two or three hours before the ceremony of the *satti,* and she demanded of Ambar that he bring her word of Jodh Bai's fate. Within a few hours he had the tidings she wished.

The girl had appeared at the pit where her husband's body lay on the piled-up wood, within a cabin of cedar and sandalwood. After the Brahmans had set fire to it, she walked about the pit, giving away her armlets and jewels to women in the throng that watched. Apparently she had been drugged, because she staggered often and had to be supported. At times she crooned to herself, and then she wept.

After it was clear to the watchers that she was unable to throw herself into the flames, now filling the pit, the Brahmans had thrust at her with the long poles they used to stir the fire. Apparently by accident they caused her to stumble at the edge of the pit; but one of the poles had thrust her into the fire. Once she screamed.

Jodh Bai had been taken from Nur Mahal's protection, as Maryam had been snatched from her, unseen, by the forces that demanded victims.

"It was written," Ambar concluded, "and even the Most Gracious could not prevent."

Secretly, he was relieved. It seemed to the old man that Nur Mahal had defied the laws that safeguarded the veiled women too often herself to venture to interfere with others. Even now, as she heard his tale, a cloudy, bitter look had come upon her, and this he knew was an omen of further trouble.

"And have we not trouble enough already?" he complained to Hushang, the Persian eunuch who was as faithful as a dog to his lady. "Perhaps for one moon, perhaps for two, thou and I shall eat and drink as now. Then we shall taste the bowstring or the scimitar's edge. Oh, God, if our lady had not broken pardah."

Hushang nodded thoughtfully, fingering the beads at his throat. "Ay, so it may be. But where is the hand that can strip my lady of favor if Jahangir still desires her? No person can take her place, for Prithvi now satisfies him only with opium and caresses. The Hindu is only one, while our lady—" he paused to contemplate a fresh idea (he was not a philosopher)—"our lady hath a different nature for every man."

"Then she hath too many. To rule men from behind the curtain, that is lawful and good," Ambar maintained stubbornly. "To go out like this against the law will turn men against her, and arm the women her enemies. *Vai*—your words are water, sinking into sand. Arslan is wearing white garments. He knows."

Devout Moslems often put on white when facing danger, so that death might find them fittingly clad. Hushang smiled. "And hath our lady not worn white these many years?"

"Words!" Ambar snarled. "What are words?"

In spite of their misgivings, the two who were responsible for Nur Mahal's seclusion—and who could no more restrain her than they could pen water from a broken dam—waited eagerly to see what action she would take. Secretly they both hoped she would disobey Jahangir and return with them to Ajmere. It was dangerous to remain away, while Jahangir's passion might cool, and while her enemies had his ear. She did not even write or send a token, as the weeks passed—only busied herself in the courtyard with suppliant women who were too overwhelmed with calamity to be aided by any human power. At times she sat among her working maids, watching the progress of new embroideries or sketching the design of gold plate, to be finished by the goldsmiths. For the most part she sat by the stone fretwork of the gallery, looking into the starlight and singing to herself.

Hushang, who understood women with the insight of his kind, knew that she was happy, and thought vaguely that this was because she could rest without having to meet the demands of Jahangir's passion. He had forgotten Lardili.

Then an amazing thing happened. The daughter of Jaggat Singh came to her door as a suppliant.

The Hindu woman was one of Jahangir's younger wives, little noticed. He had married her a dozen years before, to create a blood tie with one of the greatest of the Hindu lords; so she became leader of the Hindu house, too proud of her birth to take open notice of either Nur Mahal or Prithvi. Now she came in undisguised tears, and plunged into lamentation without ceremony.

"My lord—" even in her grief she disdained to speak of Jahangir as the husband of the Persian— "hath given consent to surrender Prince Khusrau."

Nur Mahal glanced at her with quick interest. Khusrau was Jahangir's first-born, of a Rajput mother; he had rebelled against his father, on advice of the Rajputs, almost before Jahangir had seated himself firmly on the throne. Then Khusrau had been implicated in an attempt to poison Jahangir— and had been blinded by his father's orders, being kept thereafter under loose guard. But the prince had always been liked by the people; now his blindness and captivity brought him the reverence of the multitudes, and they followed him about when he appeared in public on a horse or elephant with his guard of Rajput troopers. It was said he had recovered the sight somewhat in one eye. So Khusrau became a leading figure in the question of the succession. As eldest son, and as general favorite—and as a pawn thrust forward by the great nobles who were

antagonistic to Kurram—he had a claim to be Jahangir's heir. Meanwhile Kurram, victorious and
possessed of his father's favor, remained the openly
acknowledged heir.

"To surrender him to whom?" she demanded.

"To his brother, Prince Kurram."

It seemed incredible. True, Kurram and Khusrau
had no personal quarrel; but between them lay the
right to succession to an empire, and the elder was
almost helpless.

"How was it done?"

"It is not yet done, O daughter of Ghias Beg. The
order only has been given." The Hindu lifted her
head proudly. "As thou knowest, Prince Khusrau is
in the keeping of Rai Singh Dalan, who is a man of
honor with the rank of four thousand. When they
came with the order he made answer that he had received his charge from the hand of the emperor, and
to no other would he deliver him. Ay, he and his
four thousand would die at the gate rather than deliver the prince."

"Who brought the order?"

"An armed guard, servants of Prince Kurram and
thy father, Ghias Beg."

"And then, what?" Not by the least dropping of
eyelids did Nur Mahal betray her astonishment at
her father's name.

"They went away. No doubt to Kurram, at Ajmere, to gain my lord's written consent for Rai Singh
Dalan to deliver the Prince."

This being all the information she needed, the
Persian waited for the Hindu to say more. Reluc-

tantly, the sallow woman, whose only ornament was a string of black pearls, explained that Khusrau's sisters and relatives in the harem were grief stricken— "They are ready to scatter their ashes on the wind of death." Yielding to their entreaty she had come to beg—proudly, she did not shirk the word for a softer one—the Light of the Palace to use her influence with Jahangir, to permit Khusrau to remain where he was, in safety.

To the Hindu's surprise, Nur Mahal only said, "I am honored by the visit of the daughter of Jaggat Singh."

When the Hindu had gone, Nur Mahal sent at once for her father. He had the right of entry to her rooms, although he seldom came, being the busiest man in all India. Late that evening he appeared, a grave man, much stooped yet immaculate in dress, with a great blue sapphire dangling from his turban. He acknowledged his daughter's salaam and seated himself slowly, his glance roving among the gold candelabra and jeweled trays. Ghias Beg had a taste for jewels, and a weakness for the trappings of wealth.

"Thy health, Mihri, how——"

For once she interrupted her father, being in no patient mood.

"What truth is there in the talk that you have joined with Kurram in demanding the person of Khusrau?"

"Truth?" The old Persian lifted his brows. "We obey the order of the Padishah thy lord."

"An order given at the third watch of the night!"

It was a pure guess; but she knew that Jahangir
would have been in his cups at that hour, and might
have signed an order that he would reject in the day.
Ghias Beg considered his blue-veined hands impassively. He had discovered long since Nur Mahal
might be kept in ignorance, but could not be deceived. So he remained silent.

"Who thought of it first—you, my father?"

He shook his head moodily. "Kurram wished it. It
concerns thee not, my daughter."

"It lies heavily upon the hearts of those who love
the blind prince. It is wrong, to put him within Kurram's power."

Ghias Beg spoke quietly, his fine voice giving
music to the eloquent Persian phrases. Kurram had
no thought except the honor of his house—had he not
been devoted to Akbar, and faithful to his father?
He was about to set out with the army for a new
campaign in the far south. Khusrau's followers had
been causing trouble, raising the smoke of dissension
over the hidden fire of rebellion. To place Khusrau
in Kurram's hands would be a guaranty of truce, and
would also safeguard the blind prince from Kurram's followers—since Kurram's honor would be at
stake, for his safety.

"Still," Nur Mahal smiled, chin on hand, "it is
wrong."

"It is expedient."

"So expedient that the order was given to my lord
to sign when he lay drunk!"

Ghias Beg started. He was a faithful servant of
the emperor—the matter of a few bribes concerned

only himself—and he believed devoutly that in Jahangir lay vested the authority of God on earth.

"What hath come upon thee, Mihri?"

She had been wondering what intrigue was behind the seemingly innocent removal of Khusrau. Instinct warned her that it would be safer for Jahangir to have two claimants for the throne among his sons. More than that she did not reason. "Oh, say that it is curiosity," she responded.

"Take the wheat, but leave the stubble to the gleaners, my daughter. Until now thou hast not meddled with matters of state, and it is not well for a woman to do so."

Absently she nodded. "Would you alone have asked for that order?"

Again Ghias Beg kept silence, until he bethought him of a real anxiety. "It is now two moons since thou hast left the mahal of thy lord the emperor, upon whom be the mercies of God. Is it not time for thee to return to his couch?"

"You wish it, my father?"

"Who would not?"

From beneath the tangle of dark hair her eyes lifted to his briefly. "Oh, it is so quiet in Agra. I wish my tomb could be like this."

A vague qualm stirred the Diwan of the Empire, and he stifled it with common sense. "Thou art not safe within the plague's taint. Nay, surely thy beauty hath no need of a tomb. I have heard that Jahangir awaits thee impatiently, having sent messages commanding thy presence."

"Messages? When?"

"Two at least, my daughter. I know not the time —that thou must know."

"They never reached my hand."

"Then go to Ajmere! Avert calamity, and hasten, to beg forgiveness of thy lord."

Suddenly she flung up her head. "Why, certainly I shall go, tomorrow. Verily I the favorite should be at the couch of my lord."

And Ghias Beg took his leave, gratified at the success of his call. That night, after Lardili had curled herself up on a couch, Nur Mahal sat late at the stone lattice looking out, although there was no moon, and a haze dimmed the starlight. Her maids, waiting up drowsily, thought that for one so lovely the Persian spent little time in gazing into mirrors and too much in looking at nothing.

Three nights later in the Bath-house of the lash-gar under Ajmere's walls, Jahangir amused himself at cards with a chosen company, while Prince Kurram paced the anteroom waiting until the guests should be dismissed. It was long past the middle of the night, but Jahangir was not yet in a mood to sleep. He had summoned the new English envoy out of bed to sit beside him; and from time to time he leaned over to show this *Inglisi khan*—he could not master the name Sir Thomas Roe—the cards in his hand.

In honor of the bluff Englishman, upon whom the other nobles looked with curious disgust, Jahangir had placed against the wall paintings of King James, and a fleet fighting with another fleet at sea.

"They are passable," he remarked, studying his hand. "Yet my painters could copy them so skillfully that you would not be able to tell them apart."

Even in his cups—and they had been drinking spirits—Sir Thomas was a diplomat. Besides, he had learned that any game into which the Mogul enticed him he must lose. "I venture not," he responded, and the Portuguese priest who had been called in to interpret, repeated the words in Hindi.

"You can't tell them, or you won't try?" Jahangir was always a stickler for accuracy.

"A copy could not be like the original," the English ambassador maintained. (And the Portuguese, who desired nothing more than the disgrace of this stubborn envoy, explained, "His Majesty's painters could not possibly equal these.")

"Will you bet?" demanded Jahangir, interested.

"As Your Majesty pleases."

"A dress of honor, then, against a bolt of blue velvet." (The dress costs only a few rupees, while Jahangir would have had to pay three gold pieces for the velvet.)

Satisfied, he commanded that the paintings be taken away to his artists, who should set to work at once, to have a half-dozen copies ready in twenty-four hours. He added that he would have them beaten if the originals could be told from the copies.

"Your coach," he observed to the Englishman, "is very pretty, but it has no place for a family in it."

The sallow Portuguese explained that the Mogul meant a woman when he said family.

"In my land," Sir Thomas ventured, "we did not know that the family of His Majesty rode in carriages." (And the priest interpreted, "In his country they did not think the mahal of the Padishah worthy to ride in such a fine carriage.")

For a moment Jahangir frowned. Then he remarked to the attentive Farrash that these English were undoubtedly barbarous animals who knew little of the world.

"Verily," assented the poet, "they bark like dogs. Only Allah knows how they sing."

This gave Jahangir an idea, and after pressing a cup of spirits on the reluctant ambassador, he urged him to sing something that the English liked. There was no refusing the Mogul in such a mood, and Sir Thomas cleared his throat and rose on sturdy legs—he had left his shoes at the gate, and wore a pair of the Mogul's indoor slippers.

A broad man, with a florid, worried face, who yet carried himself with dignity. He fingered the ruff at his throat, bowed to Jahangir, and began a ballad of the sea. His hoarse voice mellowed as he fell into the cadence of it.

> *"The King sits in Dunfermline toun*
> *Drinking the blude-red wine:*
> *'O whaur will I get a skeely skipper*
> *To sail this gude ship of mine?'"*

"What is it about?" Jahangir whispered to the priest.

"Alas, Majesty, 'tis a strange sound like the growling of beasts, yet it hath to do with ships that were wrecked at sea."

"Then it must be thy fleet that was overthrown by the Inglisi this year." Jahangir had not forgotten the drubbing administered to the Portuguese off Surat, and his chief reason in favoring the uncouth English, who sent him no better gifts than hunting dogs and a great stagecoach, was to have a check at sea upon the power of the insolent Portuguese.

> *" 'I saw the new moon late yestreen,*
> *Wi' the auld moon in her arm;*
> *And I fear, I fear, my master dear,*
> *That we sall come to harm!' "*

When Sir Thomas ended his ballad the Mogul felt weary of entertainment and dismissed the company. He was still fumbling over the cards on the carpet, trying to separate the twelve kings from the others—he knew there should be twelve kings, one on a horse, one on an elephant, another sitting in a throne, and he could not seem to assemble all the twelve at once—when Kurram stood beside him. Somehow the sharp outline of his son's fine head displeased him at that moment.

"Thou art like a fox, Joyous," he exclaimed, and the secretary behind him hid a smile. Jahangir had ordered that all his words during these evening bouts be taken down and shown to him the next day; also that any order of execution he might sign should be delayed until the next sunset. Kurram, with his long head, his tawny close-set eyes, and sharply trimmed beard, did resemble a fox somewhat. Yet a dignified and sagacious fox. "Or a skeleton at the banquet."

Jahangir heard his son's cold voice mention a personal order to be given, having to do with Khusrau. "Was not that settled?" he interrupted. "Harken, Joyous, to a strange thing. I dismounted Sunday from my horse beside a tank. In the middle of the tank stood a stone building, with pillars. On one of the pillars I saw this quatrain of somebody or other cut:[1]

> *"'The friends who drank Life's draught with me*
> *have gone.*
> *Content with less than I, they one by one*
> *Laid down their cups to take Death's waiting hand,*
> *In silence, 'ere the Feast was well begun.'"*

When he paused, Kurram felt called upon to comment.

"It is not bad, O my father, but I see nothing strange in it."

"Nothing strange that I should find it by chance in a ruin? I laid my hand on the pillar, and there was the quatrain. Only God knows who wrote it, yet he had a true appreciation of wine." Jahangir nodded

---

[1] Jahangir had chanced upon one of the best of Omar Khayyam's quatrains. The present writer has made the translation above from the original Persian, which differs a little from Fitzgerald's well-known rendering:

> *"For some we loved, the loveliest and the best*
> *That from his Vintage rolling Time hath prest,*
> *Have drunk their Cup a Round or two before,*
> *And one by one crept silently to rest."*

reflectively. "Old boy, Kurram, thou hast neither philosophy nor a taste for wine."

The prince acquiesced in silence. "The order waits," he observed after a moment, "to permit Rai Singh Danap to deliver Khusrau."

Jahangir tried to remember the circumstances, and found himself staring at the points of flame above the candles. Carefully he counted them, and assured himself there were seven, but perhaps twice seven. To deliver Khusrau?

Of course it should be done. He had always cherished a fondness for the blind prince, and he had called in the most learned physicians in an attempt to restore Khusrau's sight after the blinding.

"The order is written," Kurram's voice assured him, "as your Majesty desired, yet Rai Singh Danap must have your auspicious handprint." He nodded to the secretary, who hastened to moisten a square of red paint large enough to color a human hand.

Meanwhile Jahangir had taken the written scroll and was studying the lines of minute script that wavered in strange fashion, escaping his eyes. Yes, it was necessary to give his handprint to the order.

"Does it not affect my honor that Khusrau should be safe?" he asked vaguely.

Kurram had waited in the anteroom for hours to make certain that the order should be signed. Within a week he was to take command of the army journeying into the Dekkan, and he had no wish to leave his blind brother close to the court perhaps for years until his return. The plan to transfer Khusrau to his own keeping was a simple precaution; yet Kurram

never neglected precautions. Now impatience at the
sodden, wavering mind of his father overcame him.

"And is my honor also not at stake?" he demanded.

Jahangir was in no condition to reason such a fine
point. Turning the paper vaguely in his hands, he
looked for the candle flames again and drew a deep
breath of surprise. Between the candelabra stood a
woman in white who looked at him with unearthly
eyes. The light danced from the chain of sapphires
that bound her hair, and from blue stones upon wrist
and ankle and bare, slim arms—so that she seemed
to be moving although she remained motionless as a
statue. In a moment he understood that this was no
vision of Peristan, the abode of fairies, but Nur
Mahal.

Glancing at her sidewise, Kurram wondered how
long she had been listening behind the curtain, and
what perverse impulse had brought her into the
Bath-house during the hours sacred to the Mogul's
revelry. At the same time he felt the old keen delight
in her nearness—the sight of the dark head poised
beneath its sheer veil.

"Shaikhu Baba," she cried, "I have just come from
Agra. We journeyed through the evening, to reach
my lord."

With a flash of blue fire, she slipped from between
the candles to kneel by him, her head lowered to his
feet. Kurram, inwardly enraged, could not help admiring the perfect attitude of submissive loveliness,
while he glanced curiously at his father, knowing
that Nur Mahal had gone to Agra on her own whim

and had not received the messages Jahangir sent her, urging return.

"Thou hast escaped the plague, Mihri!" he exclaimed. "Why wert thou so long in coming? We have had much sickness—even I did not escape. It took me by the throat for a few days, stifling my breath, and when it passed, I had only half my wonted strength.[1] I breathe uneasily and sleep badly."

The flesh had gathered in folds about his eyes, and his lips were colorless. When he spoke he panted and coughed. Nur Mahal had noticed the change in him at her first glance. "But the hunting—it has been good?" she smiled.

Jahangir shook his head pathetically. "Mihri, I could not go. Every day during this sickness I showed my face to the people at the jharoka and administered justice."

"They had need of my lord's mercy," she murmured, "as I have."

"Thou?" He leaned forward to look more closely at the suppliant figure, vaguely conscious that in some way she had defied him. But the scent of rose leaves drove all brooding away.

Kurram, waiting in vain to hear his father reproach the Persian, shrugged his shoulders and hid the written order in his shawl girdle. Not once had Nur Mahal seemed to notice the paper, but Kurram knew that she had interrupted them to prevent

[1] Jahangir's illness was influenza, which swept India at the time of the more deadly bubonic plague which was then in Agra. He was also troubled by his usual asthma.

Jahangir signing it. "Will the Padishah," he asked formally, "grant me leave to depart?"

"Ay, go. Have them close the doors. Have no one enter beyond the curtain."

Thus he dismissed Kurram as if the greatest of the princes had been no more than a groom, and Nur Mahal did not smile. When Kurram's straight back had vanished between the curtains, Jahangir cried out at the woman who knelt beside him.

"What devil possessed thee, not to come to the presence of thy lord? Two summonses I sent."

To tell him the truth, that someone had intercepted the messages, would sound like the most futile of excuses. So a little smile touched her lips, and she whispered:

"But am I not here?"

A gray mist gathered about his eyelids, and he tried to brush it away. In his veins the opium sang to him with a murmur of rushing water and a sighing of wind—wind that drove away the gray mist, until the woman appeared to be a white shape kneeling upon white sand, while twice seven suns flared and flickered behind her head. Her face glowed from within as if it, too, were lighted.

Delirium that was like pain seized his limbs, and his hands trembled against his knees. Still the wind rushed past him, a warm wind bearing the scent of roses in the sun. The sands changed imperceptibly into a gossamer of white silk, spun by unseen hands.

His hands had pulled the light khalat from her shoulders, but his clumsy fingers could not loosen the

body cloth, wound tight upon her. "Do thou——"
he muttered.

Slowly she unwound the cloth, letting it fall with
her veil, while he leaned nearer, his dull eyes staring at the white beauty of her body.

"Look thou at me," he whispered, and his heart's
beat echoed in his head like the chiming of a muffled,
far-off bell. Clearly now he could see into her eyes,
dark with passion. But he could not see the fear that
shadowed them.

"The candles," he said. "I am a poor servant."

Turning, she stretched a slender arm to the candelabra, and blew out the flames one by one. He
could still feel the hot wind rushing by, yet he could
see nothing more in the darkness. His arm was about
her, his hand thrusting upon her breast, while her
lips caressed his throat where the heavy pulse beat.

Her hair fell against his face, blown by the same
hot wind, and he wondered why, when the sun had
gone with its light, its heat should linger. The pain
that was sheer delight crept through his body, until
it gathered into the throbbing of his head. His arms
were quivering against her firm, quiet body, and his
strength had turned into the water that slipped by
so soundlessly.

She lay quiet against him, and he wondered why
he was listening to that strange wind. It had brought
a fever that burned him, without touching her. He
breathed heavily, turning his head to draw air into
his lungs. And as he did so, she freed herself gently
from his arms.

"It is the sickness that weighs on me," he gasped.

She lifted his head and moved so that it rested against her knee; with the end of her veil she wiped the sweat from his forehead and cheeks; then she groped along the rug for a peacock's plume, and fanned him quietly. "Ay, the sickness. O my life, you should not tire yourself thus. It is better to rest and sleep."

"Daily I sat in the jharoka, while they carried forth the sick. . . . This weakness will pass, God willing . . . now thou art come."

When she put down the fan an hour later and drew her khalat over her shoulders, Jahangir slept heavily. Gray light crept into the curtained room, under the canopy, and showed his face a gray mask upon her knee. The pictured cards took shape on the rug, among the disordered cups. Nur Mahal, sitting motionless, unsleeping, turned her mind's vision back through the years. Before her hung a tapestry with figures of huntsmen riding down lions, but she saw it not.

She was Mihri again, little older than Lardili—there in the balcony of the red city, watching the young prince striding among the flowers. A magic hour, in which her eyes feasted upon the turn of his head, and a shiver went through her when she fancied that he looked toward the balcony. Precious moments when she heard his laugh, and knew that he was pleased. . . . Her doll had a bright, new painted face then, and she whispered to it of love.

That was one delightful memory—until she had been hurt at the garden pool. And then hastened into

the arms of the Tiger Thrower, who had enjoyed her
beauty and had understood less of her than of his
horses. . . . Her beauty that had not escaped the
searching eyes of another man, in power. The Tiger
Thrower had wearied of home dwelling. He had
followed the armies too long, and the other was
Kutb ud-Din, milk brother of Jahangir, governor of
the *subah* of Bengal, whose servants could carry a
woman to his tent. A daring man, who for a little
space had worshipped her, and whose child Lardili
was.

Lardili she had, and the muslin doll with the face
worn away . . . when Jahangir had taken her into
his arms again, she had been pleased for a little, seeing in him the emperor, the man who served God
among the multitudes. And the splendor of it gratified her, who had always longed for precious things.
Now he had become this gray mask, lying inert on
the disordered rug.

She had done nothing of her own will—she had
consented to it all. Stolen hours of freedom she had
found for herself. Only to be hunted like the lions—
in the full daylight she saw the figures of the tapestry
take shape—by the huntsmen. And she wanted so
much—what did she want? To have a refuge of her
own, secure even from her father's command and
Jahangir's importunity . . . and the unseen enemies
that pulled at her feet.

Jahangir she could influence, and mold to her will.
But he was stubborn, and beset by the forces at work
against her. . . . He, the emperor, could not safeguard his wife. Nor the pitiful throng that waited

outside her door for protection. And she had sought
nothing for herself until now. She had become a
gilded figure of a golden court, passive as the very
carpet beneath her. She was embroidered upon a
tapestry, hunted by armed men who were following,
following close. . . .

With a quick indrawn sigh, she saw a refuge she
could reach. Protection for herself, and others—
safety for Lardili. If she could only draw power into
her own hands! To have the right to issue commands
from the Throne—lands and armed forces of her
own—to make men dependent upon her, by this very
power that would be hers to give or to withhold. If
she could gain this, in her own name, even as a
woman, she could safeguard the sick man who slept
so uneasily against her knee.

Before that year ended, Jahangir wrote down in
his memoirs that he had granted to Nur Mahal the
style of Nur Jahan. The Light of the Palace by his
wish had become Light of the World. And he smiled
when he first watched her sign in her quick, deft
strokes an imperial *firman*.

But it was Farrash the poet who gave expression
to the subtle change that had taken place in Nur
Mahal.

"We have lost a favorite," he declared, "and we
have gained an empress."

IV

IX years passed.

They were years of tranquillity, bringing to Ghias Beg a satisfaction beyond words. He felt that he had never understood the extraordinary nature of his daughter until now, when she aided him in the administration of the empire.

He also had received a new title, Itimad daulat—Reliance of the State. With the title went the right to have a standard carried before him, and the privilege of having his drums beaten after those of Prince Kurram, the heir. His pay had grown enormously, amounting now to the pay of fourteen thousand horsemen. And no one but the old Persian knew how much poured into his private coffers in the way of gifts and bribes. It made a true flood of gold, and it satisfied the avaricious side of his nature.

Ghias Beg knew that he was in reality the reliance

of the empire. The Moguls ruled as conquerors, and all the wealth of India belonged to Jahangir the Padishah. When an amir died, his lands, buildings, horses and treasure escheated to the Throne, until Jahangir decided what was to be given back to the widow or sons. Living nobles, struggling for favor, paid lavishly for rare jewels to be offered the Throne. And all this tide of wealth, in its ebb and flow, passed through the accounts of Ghias Beg's treasury.

It needed a wizard to keep accounts of such stupendous nature, and Ghias Beg managed to balance them as if with a magician's wand, to his own profit.

Like the other grandees upflung by this tide of treasure, he lived lavishly. What avail to amass coins or land, when everything passed to the hands of the imperial collectors at a man's death? He had built in the last six years a new palace facing the Agra River, between the great edifices reared by his son Asaf Khan and Prince Kurram. Clay bricks and sandstone flung together, and lined with blue tiles from Herat, floored with mosaics of black and white marble—with sandalwood doors and porticoes banded in lapis-lazuli set with cat's eyes. He took keenest delight in contemplating the inscription on the wall of his library—gold Arabic lettering set in ebony.

"Ye shall taste that which ye have stored up for yourselves."

Not that he fancied he could take his possessions to that Paradise where large-eyed damsels awaited him upon the couches in ever-blooming gardens. But he had accumulated wealth with a secret purpose. Although he spent with open hands, he bought valuables—jewels for his collections, ivory carvings from Cathay, the finest of rugs, strong young elephants for his stables, and always more land.

All this seemed to be destined to pass into Jahangir's capacious treasury. And because the Persian Diwan obviously had only a few more years to live, the Mogul looked upon his growing wealth with an indulgent eye. Yet Ghias Beg fancied that his property would not pass to the imperial exchequer. Never did he voice this hope; he merely contemplated the gleaming inscription which assured him on no less authority than that of the Prophet that he might taste in some fashion the riches he was storing up.

Ghias Beg did not ponder the ethics of his case. He served Jahangir in his fashion faithfully. The taxation of the multitudes—one third of the produce of the soil was claimed by the district agents for the Throne—he knew to be excessive. At the same time, the rule of the Moguls gave some compensation. From the mountain peaks of Kabul to the crowded jetties of Calcutta, there was peace.

Very wisely, after the first conquest, the Moguls granted social freedom to the conquered. True, the Hindus held to their own involved caste restrictions and nobility; but before the Throne they were all upon an equal footing. Jahangir, outwardly a Moslem, extended his favor to Buddhists and Brahmans, Jains, and even to the Christians whose holy pictures he ordered hung on the walls of his sleeping quarters.

In the villages the elders ruled without interference from above. If a hunting expedition of the

Mogul trampled the crops of a countryside, or the
mighty lashgar stripped fodder and food in its passage, the peasants could claim indemnity. If they
were fortunate enough to attract Jahangir's attention
they would be paid—because the emperor prided
himself on his administration of justice. Before
Ghias Beg held office, the villages had less land under
cultivation, and suffered more under the taxes.

Inevitably the grandees of the court, and all whose
fortunes were attached to the Throne, lived luxuriously, knowing that their property could not be
handed down to their children. Yet in a way this re-
sulted in the rise of men of character. Ghias Beg had
noticed that after three or four generations, the children of the original conquerors—the Turks and Tartars from the colder regions beyond Kabul—failed
to hold their own in the struggle with the native-
born Hindus and Moslems.

He could even trace out this change in the characters of the Moguls themselves. Babar, the conqueror a hundred years before, had been a true
Tartar—untiring in bodily strength, a boisterous
gentleman who could laugh at his own vices. Humayun his son had been cast in softer mold, adventuring
where his father had subdued. Akbar, however, had
flamed forth with startling intelligence; he had built
the city of Fathpur to satisfy his craving for expression in stone.

"Night and day change as before," Ghias Beg
would remark, "and the stars walk as of old, but
India no longer has such men."

They had all been engaged in the vast work of

conquest and establishing order. Jahangir was the first to come to the Throne as a ruler, and Ghias Beg admitted to himself that Jahangir had been a wiser man than he seemed. For one thing, the Mogul had been content to carry out Akbar's plan of government. He was not capable of planning a city like Fathpur, but Fathpur, lacking adequate supply of good water, had been abandoned. Jahangir remained indifferent to monuments; in fact, the asute Persian understood that Jahangir managed well enough simply by letting matters take their course. This policy suited the Mogul's disposition exactly.

Jahangir did not even bother to keep together a really effective army. While the great lashgar with its barbaric splendor answered the purpose of impressing the multitudes, it was no more than a great parade. It could not have stood its ground against the hard-fighting hosts of Tamerlane; yet to the peoples of India it seemed the embodiment of a vast power.

Actual fighting, of course, was necessary along the frontiers. This task Jahangir left to the ablest of his generals—Raja Bikramajit having command upon the southern fringe of the Dekkan, while Mahabat Khan held grimly to the mountain passes of the Afghans. The people of the frontiers understood only the rule of force, the sword bringing punishment for bloodshed.

So Ghias Beg had reason to be content. The empire first conceived by Tamerlane, begun by Babar, and established by Akbar, now ran its course smoothly under the rule of a much weaker man, Jahangir.

This was due not so much to Jahangir's indolent common sense as to the ability of the men who had in their hands the actual administration—to himself, Prince Kurram, and Asaf Khan. And to the integrity of Mahabat Khan. They were all, except the prince, strangers drawn into the empire by the lure of its wealth. The empire of the Mogul rested at last upon firm foundations, and the fame of it spreading through Asia brought to it an ever increasing stream of men of letters and scientists. Even from Cathay they brought their contribution of wisdom. The court of India had become the most intelligent as well as the most sophisticated of earth's kingdoms.

At times Ghias Beg discussed with the ministers of the Diwan the future growth of the empire—the increasing trade with the Far East, the opening of European commerce through the astute Portuguese and the barbarous English, the accumulation of an imperial treasure that would provide against famines. If peace could be preserved, India might enter upon a new golden age as in the lifetime of Asoka or the Guptas. The Mogul conquerors had brought peace to the land.

In the sanctuary of his palace he could anticipate this new era. But when he rode through the city he saw the plague warning upon the doors that had been sealed years before and not opened; he saw skeletons of men casting nets for fish in the muddy river; he heard the ceaseless wail of beggars:

"Yah hukk, yah hakk! Affliction waits at the gate!"

The sick prayed in the temple yards, while the conches blared. Men who were akin to animals haunted the forests, living on roots and stolen grain and shunning the ruins of older temples. Blind men holding to the blind, led by a boy or dog, sought along the roads for a miracle to give them sight.

It seemed to him that this was a land of multitudes following different paths very patiently. A land unchanging, watched over by a million priests who knew how to appease suffering with talk of the gods. They had served these gods before the coming of the Moguls—they had seen other conquerors come and sink into the mass of humanity upon whose bodies rested the Throne.

"Truly," Ghias Beg echoed the proverb, "is this a land to be ruled by a conqueror, a woman, or the will of God."

That season the rains came down with unleashed violence, for the first time in six years—filling the rivers with gray floods that wiped out fords and gnawed at villages. The forest mesh bent and steamed under the deluge, and the Jumna roared with a new voice past Agra's wall. Old *shaikhs,* weather-wise, said that these rains would drive out the last of the plague.

Forced to keep within doors, Ghias Beg overlooked his writers and accountants, copying the reports that mud-stained couriers brought in from the *subahdars* of provinces. There were lists of cattle, appraisals of land, tax receipts, and bundles of papers from the smaller *sarkars* and their villages. Reports

of treasure on the road, complaints against thieves—
dhak runners bearing missives from the imperial
lashgar, demanding in the name of the Padishah
everything from shipments of gold to turquoise stud-
dings for palkis, and apples to be rushed from Kabul.
Only the important accounts were brought to Ghias
Beg, where the Diwan sat apart from the bustle of
work. Above the white, clipped beard, his thin face
had grown to parchment hue, but the meditative
brown eyes were clear and searching as always. From
time to time he whispered to the confidential writer
behind him, who made cryptic notes in Persian.
While he listened to his secretaries Ghias Beg managed to follow the tales of visitors who had paid
heavily for the privilege of talk with the magician
of the Treasury. He gave them all the untiring attention of the aged and active mind that needed little
sleep.

On a night when the rains were nearly ended and
the stars could be seen above the dark, drenched
roofs, he was told that his son Asaf Khan awaited
him in the library, having come from the lashgar
with word for him.

Ghias Beg was engaged with a Chinese merchant
from Khoten who had promised to deliver twenty
camel loads of the clearest green-veined jade. It
would have to be brought over the snow passes of
Tibet, but the Diwan did not concern himself with
that. He was particular about the quality of the jade
and the shaping of the pieces, and he smiled slightly
when the dealer mentioned a price.

"I am not buying for the Treasury," he explained.

"The jade, Ch'ien Mu, I desire as a gift to my daughter."

The Chinese bowed assent, and reduced his price from seven hundred thousand rupees to six, while he wondered what even Nur Mahal could want of a caravan load of jade.

"If it be as you have described, Ch'ien Mu, I will pay five hundred thousand, and forty thousand for the transport in advance. No more." Ghias Beg rose, taking the arm of a servant. "I shall not see many more rains, Ch'ien Mu, and soon you will use your arts to cheat another Diwan. I give the green veined jade to my daughter, to line my tomb."

In his library, among the cabinets of manuscripts, Ghias Beg found his son rising to salute him. Asaf Khan had grown rounder with the years, his dark beard framing the sallow moon of his face. As usual, he wore a khalat of ceremony, stiff with gold embroidery.

"As God is my witness, O my father," he cried, "your health is a fire to warm our hearts."

"I live, yes, and I work." Ghias Beg had grown sparing of words, but his thin voice still had its music. "What is the news from the lashgar?"

Smacking his lips over handfuls of sugar candy the servants hastened to bring him, the Master of the Household related events. "The Padishah exclaimed with pleasure at your offering of the seventy-four carat sapphire, my father. I was careful to present it at a favorable moment, when he returned from watching his latest pets—two cranes. For two moons the court hath waited upon the mating of these cranes. First our lord must observe them in the act, and then notice how the pair bore themselves toward other cranes. Thereafter, it is the truth, that Jahangir fretted his spirit until the egg was laid. God willing, it came, and we rejoiced, saying that the Padishah's interest would now cease. Yet he went daily to sit and watch how first the female crane and then the male sat in turn upon the egg—the male bringing his mate food during this time. May Ali be my witness, we amirs of the lashgar asked our servants each day, 'What have the cranes done?' to learn the humor of our lord. God was merciful, and the egg hatched, giving forth a strong young one. At that time, I left.

"Our lord is in excellent temper, planning a journey to the Kashmir resorts." Asaf Khan grimaced good-naturedly. "No doubt the mountains are praiseworthy, and holy to the Hindus, but I do not relish jolting on the hill paths."

"I know. But thy tidings?"

"A new coin Jahangir designed."

Ghias Beg looked up expectantly. Jahangir had been pleased to order a fresh set of gold pieces that shocked orthodox Moslems. Not only did the emperor insert upon them the figures of the beasts of the Zodiac but he had his own head stamped on a muhr, with a wineglass at his lips. What had he done now?

Silently Asaf Khan took a silk purse from his girdle and opened it. He held up a new coin, with two heads stamped on its face, and Ghias Beg drew a breath of amazement. Beside the profile of the emperor was that of his own daughter. On the reverse

side he read the inscription, "By order of the Ruler
Jahangir, the splendor of this gold is increased a
hundred times by the beauty of the Princess Nur
Mahal."

"Pretty?" His son smiled. "A miracle hath befallen our family that Mihri's likeness should be
shown to all as empress."

"Mihri's head!"

As his son had said, it was a miracle. The law of
Islam forbade the making of a portrait, and pious
Moslems had repeated through the centuries the
tradition that a land ruled by a woman was accursed.
And here was not only a portrait—an image of a
woman who ruled at the side of a weak husband—
but a portrait of a veiled princess upon a coin that
would be handled by common men. He wondered
swiftly if his daughter or Jahangir had thought of
it. The emperor, of course, had given the order to
the Mint; but who had wished it?

"Now, my father," Asaf Khan smiled, pushing
aside the sweets, "is our cup of triumph full. Already
hath my sister the right to sign imperial decrees, and
to sit veiled behind our lord in public audience. If
she could hold rank, as you and I, she would command thirty thousand—only less than Kurram."

"What do they say in the streets, concerning the
new coin?"

"Some laugh—which is not good. But what should
they say? The very bazaar sweepers know that
Jahangir is an empty bottle, leaning against your
daughter."

"Allah mafikh!" The old minister frowned. "God

forbid that they know it. What words are these, of
thy speaking? The Padishah Ghazi, Jahangir, is
Akbar's son, and the Lord of our Lives. Never forget that, even in thy sleep. . . . Who were they who
laughed?"

"A few amirs from the hills, and the Rajput followers of the captive Rana's son." Asaf Khan's eyes
wandered to the gold inscription above the arch of
the door. *"'Ye shall taste what ye have stored up.'*
Rather will Akbar's son taste your collections and
treasure."

"Who else? Now I wish to talk no more—I will
rest." His stout son's idle good-nature did not seem
to fit with the consummate cunning he displayed at
times. Certainly the jovial Master of the Household
had all the ability of a prime minister, but he displayed no ambition except in the magnificence of his
feasts. When he had departed, leaving a scent of
musk in the room, Ghias Beg turned the coin over
between his delicate fingers.

A miracle! Forty years before, he had been master
of only three animals. He had been forced to beg the
Kandahar caravan to wait, while Mihri was born
behind saddlecloths, to screen the mother from the
eyes of the camel men. Now he counted his rupees
by the lakhs, and his camels by the thousand . . .

He asked his servant to bring from his treasury a
certain tray of matched amethysts and odd jewels.
For a while he admired the color of the stones, and
pondered how he might have the larger ones cut, to
give out more fire. But his thoughts would not stray
from his daughter. After all, it was no miracle.

When he had been treasurer of Kabul city, and she had first put on a veil at eight years, she had brought her dolls into the garden to sit by him while he did his day's work. And she had understood—her slim hands had been quick at counting the copper *dams* he gave her. She had learned much of men and their moods.

For the last six years he had lent her guidance—had seen how her wit cut through the tangle of a problem. She made decisions instantly, impatiently. And Ghias Beg wondered if a woman's intelligence might not match the book- and custom-fed minds of men. But that was absurd. Nur Mahal's very intensity of feeling had brushed aside difficulties until now. Still her power rested upon no firmer foundation than her beauty and her influence over Jahangir.

Before lying down, Ghias Beg wrote a letter to his daughter with his own hand. The letter was no more than two lines of flowing Persian verse:

*"Is it not known to thee that the gold coin
Of pride can be melted by the acid of envy?"*

To prying eyes the words meant nothing; to Nur Mahal they would be a warning. Within a week he received an answer, beautifully inscribed on scented rice paper:

*"I serve love alone, and the seventy-and-two
Sects of the faithless are known to me."*

At first Ghias Beg smiled indulgently, aware that his daughter had capped his impromptu verses by quoting from Hafiz. Then he became grave. She had read his warning aright and had brushed it aside. The love that she served—it would be Jahangir's. The rest of the poem required a little thought, even from an astute Persian. Moslems believed there were seventy-three religious sects in the world, of which one alone was to be saved in the after life. The faithless, of course, were her enemies. So she declared that she sought nothing in life beyond her love, and she was aware of the plotting of her foes.

True, she had made her position more secure by the marriage of her daughter Lardili to the youngest of the princes, an amiable and lovely lad, born of a Hindu concubine. Shahriyar, as they called him, had no prospect of the Throne, since his three elder brothers were born of legitimate wives, yet he was a favorite of the court.

While he waited for the last of the rains, Ghias Beg sent eyes and ears to listen to the talk in the bazaars and serais and mosque porticoes. His agents returned with various tales. The masses were indifferent as yet to the dominance of Nur Mahal. Few others dared mention her openly, but some adherents of the blind prince Khusrau complained of the favor she continued to show Kurram, who now had his brother in his keeping. Certain *mullahs* grumbled with religious zeal that a land ruled by a woman would be accursed. And there was talk in the north of a sign seen in the sky.

"For eight nights appeared a luminous shaft, rising from the earth and taking the shape of a spear with a flowing tail. Each night it rose a little earlier. It moved slowly across the stars and disappeared with the dawn. Astrologers say that such spears in the sky portend weakness to kings. But only God, the Knower of Secrets, knows the truth."

Idle minds connected this omen with the rise of Nur Mahal's fortune. India, in the memory of men, had never been so dominated by a woman. Other lands of Islam had never known such power gathered into the hands of a curtained woman. So the idlers discussed her, more curious than disturbed. Certainly all agreed that the last ten years, since her marriage to the Padishah, had brought peace and well being.

But Ghias Beg was not satisfied. In the bazaar gossip he could detect no undernote of menace, and outwardly all seemed auspicious. Perhaps the very quiet disturbed him, who had learned to listen unceasingly for the whisper of coming storms. He felt listless, and spent more time over his trays of jewels than in the treasury—until he decided to journey to the lashgar which was then on its way into Kashmir.

Nur Mahal was with it. She had guided its course away from Agra for the last five years—ostensibly to keep Jahangir out of the plague belt, in reality to keep him moving about, hunting and leading the semblance of his army, away from the multitudes and the fleshpots of the great cities.

Ghias Beg ordered his horse litter and road followers, and traveled steadily until he came up with the "tail" of the great moving camp in the foothills. He found his daughter superintending the finishing of a garden with a sun seat, and they went together to her pavilions.

"Hast thou forgotten, Mihri," he said after a moment, "that it is well to cover the fire of ambition with the ashes of discretion?"

She looked at him in silence.

"There is much talk in Agra of the new coin," he went on. "The mullahs are buzzing like bees when the hive is shaken, and they have put a saying on the lips of men—that a land ruled by a woman is accursed."

"The new coin was my lord's wish," she replied simply. "And I cannot alter men's talk."

Ghias Beg shook his head slightly. He found it hard to argue with his daughter, who had an uncomfortable way of clinging to the truth. From the lacquer traveling case he had brought with him, he took several closely written sheets and handed them to her, watching the quick play of her eyes as she read.

"That is a list of all my property—the little wealth that God has deigned to entrust to me," he explained. "Yet it is much more than people believe is between my hands. I have kept it intact for a purpose."

"It is much."

The old Persian smiled, as if he had been paid a compliment. "Let the praise be to God! This will all be thine."

Nur Mahal did not seem astonished; she had guessed her father's purpose long since. "But how?"

Leisurely he told her what he had cherished in his mind. Already she had wealth more than enough for her needs; his lands and collections would make her one of the wealthiest souls in Asia—would give her physical resources equal to the greatest amirs or Prince Kurram. And if she begged it of Jahangir, the Mogul would turn over her father's holdings to her. Jahangir enjoyed making such imperial gifts, and the royal inspectors did not credit Ghias Beg with half his actual possessions. No one, then, except herself need know the total.

Although she thanked him quietly, she seemed to meditate on other possibilities, until she smiled suddenly. "Then will I have a standard and the right of beating my drums at court before the princes—except Kurram!"

"God forbid," he exclaimed involuntarily. "Wilt thou never learn, Mihri, not to make display of power? Never let men read thy face."

Still she smiled. "Have they read so much in it that my father should reproach me? Surely I have learned much. Nay, come and see what I have discovered this day."

While he followed her, he wondered why the prospect of his millions had not stirred her more, and he marvelled anew when he found himself in a space enclosed by a thorn hedge. He saw some lime-washed huts, an aged man with square spectacles on his nose, and a stout man with both hands missing from his wrist. One of the huts was filled with birds on perches and in cages—every sort from quail to pigeons—and all of them bandaged.

"It is the *pinjarapul,* the bird hospital," Nur Mahal explained. "Furrukh tends the sick ones until

they are healed, when he looses them again. Show
the Diwan the mice, Furrukh."

The white-bearded keeper, moving very slowly,
brought out a box filled with cotton and a half dozen
white mice. "These are orphans," he announced,
"without mother to feed them. Will the Protector of
the Poor see how they are fed?"

When Ghias Beg gave courteous assent, Furrukh
brought a jar of milk and a small white feather.
Dipping the feather into the milk, he gave a few
drops first to one then to another of his scurrying
orphans, while Nur Mahal watched absorbedly.

"Now, in the other quarters," the keeper explained, "we have some motherless calves, which
feed without trouble, and certain cows with broken
legs."

"And thy helper?" the Diwan asked. "How
came he to lose his hands?"

"Because of a theft they were cut off, so that he
cannot now feed himself or earn wherewith to buy
food. With his arms he lifts the calves about for me
and carries water."

"Surely thy labor will earn reward from Allah
the Compassionate." Ghias Beg did not sympathize
greatly with Hindus. "And here is a little to aid thy
labor." Pulling a silver ring set with opals from his
finger, he touched it to the back of the old man's
hand.

Nur Mahal looked from one to the other expectantly, and Furrukh drew back. "May the gods
bless the giver," he murmured. "But what need have
we, O Protector of the Poor, of wealth? The hospital

costs nothing, and by favor of the princess, we have
food."

When they left the enclosure, the Persian turned
to his daughter. "Have you not cares enough, Mihri,
without this mending place of the birds?"

"It is a dissipation," she said gravely. "I go there,
not to think of money for an hour."

"But money weighs not upon thee," he laughed
gently, "who hast power to order a caravan of jade
with a word!"

"Still, I like to see the mice fed. Did it ever come
into your mind, my father, to journey back to the
hills of Khorassan? Just the two of us—and two
camels, and Arslan?"

"That day of our wandering is past, by God's
mercy." Ghias Beg thrust the silver ring back upon
his finger. "And it will never return."

"I thought not."

Something in her voice made him consider doubt-
fully. "Never hast thou set eyes upon the blue hills
of the Samarkand road, the country of my fathers.
Why are they in thy thoughts?"

"Perhaps because I have never seen them."

"Well, they are not so fair as these bulwarks of the
pagan gods." He nodded toward the line of forested
heights that showed through the heat mist to the
north. "Mihri, in a few days thou wilt see snow and
rest in Shalihmar by the lake."

"By Shalihmar—ay, the thin mountain air aids my
lord. O my father, you have lost blood and strength.
Go not back to the walls of Agra, but come with us

—send for thy cabinets and secretaries and come to the summer gardens."

Ghias Beg shook his head. "But for a while I will rest here. I feel a little tired, and perhaps"—a smile softened the white beard—"your mender of birds can teach a minister of empire how to sleep."

They were sitting on the new marble bench, discussing an appropriate inscription from Hafiz, when the eunuch Ambar hastened up and waited until Nur Mahal signed for him to approach. He had tidings from the harem, for her instant attention. When she had accompanied him into the seclusion of her cool antechamber, he broke into excited speech.

"Prithvi, the former favorite—our lord hath pronounced Dar maut upon her."

Nur Mahal exclaimed softly. The Hindu dancer to be executed, and she had known nothing of it.

"It was when the sun turned this day, O Most Imperial. They sent for Ram Bhao the Bengali eunuch to come to the carpet of the Presence. Certain ones had laid a charge against him—that he had been seen last night with the Hindu in his arms. *Ai,* true it was, and Ram Bhao confessed with tears after they had beaten the soles of his feet awhile. Then at once our master pronounced judgment, having gone without his noon sleep to hear the confession. Ram Bhao was a false servant—" the old negro's eyes gleamed contentedly—"false to his salt, and an unclean animal."

"What manner of death will they have?"

"The woman is to be strangled, the eunuch will be given to the dogs to tear apart, at sunset. Ram Bhao is fit for the dogs——"

"Be silent, thou!"

The Persian turned away from Ambar's exultation. To the negro, Prithvi and her people were enemies, whose removal would clear the thorns from the path of his mistress. Nur Mahal was thinking of other women in the harem, who had been guilty but had escaped punishment because no charge had been made against them.

Little that went on behind the curtain became known in the outer court. Yet at Agra and here in the lashgar were gathered twenty and one wives of Jahangir. During the last years he had visited few except Nur Mahal and the mothers of his sons. Only at times he became attached to some singer or new maid and summoned her to his bed.

There were hundreds of women attendants, and as many maids. A few fortunate ones, catching his attention by their beauty or skill in song, would be given away in marriage or servitude to some officer of the court—she remembered an Armenian girl whom Jahangir had insisted on marrying to the first Englishman to visit the court. But the majority of the *mahalha* saw no men, except when they looked through the curtain at the private audiences, or from the screens during a journey.

These were doomed to live without intercourse with men. Some of the Hindus took to drinking opium at night. Nur Mahal, as head of the harem, had come to know how the more daring, or the weaker among them, sought men secretly. There were cases where women had slipped from pavilions during a journey and had risked the strangling cord for a meeting with soldiers beyond the guard lines. No one had fled, because escape was impossible— their guilt would have been shared by any who hid them or talked with them.

In the last years Nur Mahal had heard of darker cases, of attachment between girls, and of young maids who had been forced to become the intimates of older habitués of the harem.

Several of the eunuchs, she knew, were paid heavily by a few women who gave them jewels and money for no apparent reason. She had seen some of the fairest concubines—slender creatures fashioned and taught for the one purpose of love—contending secretly for the favor of a stout eunuch, who was placidly pleased by their pursuit of him, while he enriched himself skillfully. Nur Mahal had ordered an Abyssinian eunuch beheaded who had extorted money from a girl who once made advances to him.

Jahangir, she thought, had not visited Prithvi or sent any gifts to the dancer for five years. Now she and Ram Bhao were to be put to death secretly at the sun setting.

"Most Imperial," Ambar had waited judiciously for her anger to subside, "is it not just? The Hindu is low-born, without shame. Remember the datura poison in the curry? Did not one of her maids visit our kitchen that evening? She hath begged for the honor of a call from the Light——"

"She asks to see me, now?"

"Truly she asks, but what need to go? When the canebrake is afire, go not to meet a tiger."

"Take me to her place. Announce me."

Characteristically, the Persian made no effort to freshen her make-up or change her garments. When she threw back the heavy head veil, after following Ambar through the pavilions, she found herself in Prithvi's sleeping chamber, the light shut out by heavy curtains, and scented oil lamps glowing on the silver wall posts. Prithvi herself lay indolently stretched upon a huge tigerskin, among silk pillows that reeked of musk. Five years had aged the former favorite, the lines of her throat had hardened, her heavily tinted lips had coarsened, and her breast seemed shapeless under the tight-drawn sari. Beneath the tangle of dark hair—no longer oiled and combed into sleek smoothness—her reddened eyes fastened upon Nur Mahal.

"Now leave us," the Persian ordered Ambar.

But the old negro's eyes opened stubbornly, and he shook his head violently. The handle of a curved knife showed above his girdle. Not if he were to be flayed alive would he have left Nur Mahal alone within reach of her enemy.

"Stand thou back," the Persian bade him, "by the curtain."

This Ambar consented to do, keeping arm's length from the drawn curtain—lest a knife be thrust into his back—and watching every motion the Hindu dancer made.

"Salaam to the Most Imperial!" Prithvi's throaty

voice greeted her. "Tomorrow Your Highness may walk to the bath and feel the sun upon her as usual, but I shall be hidden in the earth. No man's head will turn after me."

Nur Mahal waited in silence. She had expected Prithvi to beg her to intercede with Jahangir. But she could do nothing. The case had gone direct to the emperor, who had passed sentence at once. It was no longer within the curtain, and Jahangir would never pardon either the dancer or the eunuch. So she waited to learn what Prithvi wished of her. And into the opium-dulled eyes of the Hindu crept sullen envy. The Persian, slight and straight, seemed as lovely as at her first coming into the curtain. Only the lines of lips and eyebrows had been darkened.

"What wert thou," Prithvi whispered, incredulous, "when Jahangir had his will of thee—a wanton girl—in Fathpur?"

Still Nur Mahal waited. This was a chance-flung spark; the fire of Prithvi's passion was yet to be revealed and understood.

"Surely the gods have watched over thee until now. A widow, wearing white to hide the dark blood of thy first common-born husband who was ordered to wed thee after thy ravishment!"

Ambar's breath whistled between his teeth, but Nur Mahal smiled as if acknowledging truth. "Ay, I live, in spite of the datura poison."

For a moment Prithvi's eyes fell, like a chided girl's. Then she flung back her head defiantly. "By Siva, it matters not to me, who will soon taste the chill of Yama's embrace. Yet I sent before me one

dear to thee, O Light of the Palace. The girl
Maryam, who knew the secret of thy wandering
forth at night, I coaxed from thy tents years ago. We
tortured her with water that leaves no mark. She
lied to us, and so I had to slay her with the datura,
which also leaves no sign upon the body. But thou
livest, unchanged."

"And well for our master it is so," chattered Ambar from the door. "Knowest not, O Unclean, that he
hath said he knew not the meaning of marriage until
he wed my lady——"

"Be silent!" Nur Mahal commanded, and the old
eunuch held his tongue.

But Prithvi laughed shrilly. *"Ahai,* he knows it
now. . . . He knows it now. Whose hand signs the
imperial firmans and designs the new coins? May
that hand wither, although the plague did not touch
it."

"Come away, my lady," Ambar whimpered. "Behold, she curses."

"May evil dreams keep you from sleep," the voice
of the dancer shrilled on. "May the shadow of
Ganesh and the blight of Hanuman fall upon you,
until your mind knows no rest and the blood drains
from your heart. May the child of your body have
no sons because of the sickness that is worse than the
plague! May your years be many, when your hands
are empty and all men avert their faces from
you——"

"Allah forbid it to be so!" Ambar muttered,
clutching his rosary.

"—until your feet turn backward——"

"Ai—let it not be so!"

"—and your body is torn by pain as a jackal's carcase is rent by the kites, and you find no door open for you but the tomb."

"Come away, Highness!"

Prithvi dropped, panting, upon the tigerskin, her face dark, and her eyes closed.

"I have heard," Nur Mahal's clear voice assured her, "yet there is worse than that."

The Hindu dancer seemed to forget them both as she crawled toward a corner of the chamber where a figure of the god Siva stood. Beating her forehead against the ground, she sobbed with long racking breaths, gasping out prayers that Nur Mahal could not understand. Above her the bronze form of the *naturaja* poised on its toes, its six arms outflung as if summoning and repelling the three human beings. Upon the bronze lips clung a strange smile of invitation.

This figure, Nur Mahal knew, was cast in the pose of the Dancer, who invites all things to life and to death. But it seemed to her in that moment, above the sobbing woman, both cruel and evil.

"Hast thou need," she asked Prithvi, "of anything I can give?"

The dark head, wet with sweat, shook wearily. "Only bid them be quick."

Yet when the Persian had left the chamber, Prithvi clapped her hands until a frightened maid came to her.

"Write thou this," she commanded. *"To Prince Kurram in the Dekkan, greeting from the dancer,*

Prithvi. I die, may you live! Once you and I and the Persian were closest to the heart of the Padishah. Now am I sent to the grave. Watch, that your turn is not next."

Having seen this written, and sealed the folded paper with her ring, Prithvi commanded that it be sent at once by courier to the prince. It would instil a certain amount of suspicion in the alert brain of Kurram, she knew. And it seemed to restore peace to her, for she sat down by her mirror and watched the maids deck her in festive garments and all her jewels in readiness for the strangler's noose.

Long after sunset and after the last evening prayer that night, Nur Mahal lay awake by a shaded lamp with a sable wrap thrown over her and a book in her hand. It was a beautifully bound manuscript, with a portrait of Jahangir and a miniature painting of the court on its first page. That afternoon Jahangir, who appeared to have nothing else on his mind, had sent it to her. Since it was a copy of his own memoirs in Persian, she knew that she must read it and be prepared to answer any questions that might come into his mind about it. Curiously, she skimmed through the pages.

In Ahmadabad I was given two male goats. Since I had no females to pair with them, it came into my mind that I could pair them with Barbary goats. In brief, I paired them with seven Barbary ewes, and after six months had passed each of the ewes had a young one at Fathpur—four females and three males, very delightful in appearance. It is not possible to write down their laughable ways. Some of their ways are such that the mind gains enjoyment from watching. Painters find it difficult to paint goats. After a fashion they can do so, but my painters were at loss to depict the antics of these kids.

Yet the man who had dictated this had that day condemned to death the woman who had once aroused his passions. To do away, by a word, with the body that had caused him to write verses of praise! To feel nothing—no loss at the ending of a life that had been part of his . . . Nur Mahal turned the pages impatiently, pausing at the account of his latest illness in Ahmadabad.

The physicians constantly importuned me to take some gruel made of pulse and rice, but I could not manage to do so. From the time I arrived at manhood I never, so far as I recollect, drank such broth, and I hope I may never be obliged to drink it again. When such a meal was brought, I declined it. In brief, I fasted three days and three nights. I had no appetite at all.

He had not given up his wine, then, Nur Mahal reflected. And memory of his illness had embittered him against the city.

I am at loss to conceive what beauty the founder saw here, that he built a city. I should have christened it the Home of the Wind, or Abode of Sickness, or Wilderness of Thorn, or City of Hell, for all these names are appropriate.

Jahangir had an eagerness to name things. The pools and gardens of the Kashmir road had all been christened anew by him. She wondered what he would have chosen to do if he had not been emperor. To study animals and plants, without doubt, to investigate natural phenomena, and to talk to his cup companions during a never ending succession of feasts. To paint, and compare his work with that of the artists . . . Her eye was caught by his account of the latest omen from the sky.

One of the most surprising events took place in one of the villages of the *pargana* of Jalandhar. In the morning a loud and very terrible noise came from the east, frightening the inhabitants. In the midst of it a light fell from the sky, and after a moment the noise ceased. The people, much alarmed, sent a runner to Muhammad Sayyid, the governor of the district, who rode to the village. The land in one spot was so burnt for ten or twelve yards that not a blade of grass survived. The earth here was still warm. Muhammad Sayyid ordered it to be dug up, and the deeper it was dug, the warmer it became. At last a piece of iron appeared, which was as hot as if it had just been taken out of a furnace. When it cooled he placed it in a bag and sent it to me. It was weighed before me and found to weigh 160 *tolas*. . . . I ordered Master David to make a sword, a dagger, and a knife from it, but he explained that it would break into pieces under hammering. I instructed him to mix three parts of the meteoric iron with one part of common iron, and when the swords were presented I ordered them to be tried before me. They cut as well as the best tempered swords.

So, out of the omen which had excited the astrologers anew after the appearance of the flaming spear in the northern sky, Jahangir had fashioned a sword, a dagger and a knife! He was really less superstitious than the learned men. At times he took omens from Hafiz by turning to his book of the great poet at random and reading what lay under his finger, but he always noted down in the margin the results of following the auspices. For religion he had no feeling, although he went through the form of Islamic worship to satisfy his subjects. Once, after listening to a discussion between Hindu priests and Moslem mullahs, he interrupted them by asking which of all the religions permitted a man to eat and drink and do what he liked. They told him, the Christian . . . Nur Mahal noticed how frequently her own name appeared in the latest pages of the memoirs.

On the day of the *dasahra* I was seized with a catching and shortness of breath. In the air passages on my left side an oppression was felt, which gradually increased. Warm medicine gave me a little relief, but when I crossed the mountains the pain increased. I took goat's milk for several days, and tried the camel's milk which had helped me once, but neither of them did any good now. Despairing of medicine, I threw myself upon the mercy of the Universal Physician. As I found relief in drinking I resorted to it, and carried it to excess in the night. When the weather became hot, my weakness and pain increased. Nur Jahan[1] Begam, whose good sense

[1] Jahangir calls her by her new title, the Princess, the Light of the World.

exceeded that of the physicians, in her devotion, exerted herself to reduce my drinking and to provide me with more refreshing potations. Although I had cast out the doctors, I had faith in her. Gradually she cut down my wine and guarded me against the wrong food and improper things. My hope is that the True Physician may cure me.

The boyishness of it! He could not refrain from appealing to religion in these memoirs that all would read. He, who never took matters seriously, was intent upon his own health and his games. Even as emperor, he had known no real cares—the government of all India was a grave routine with him, and the hours of escape from it he devoted to his animals, his writing, and to her. In everything he clung to her. In everything, and her share was the mental anguish that escaped him so easily. . . . Nur Mahal put aside the bound manuscript and took a folded paper from a locked chest. She had read it many times before now—this copy of a letter that Jahangir had been careful to guard from her eyes.

It was from Mahabat Khan, and as she read she could see the tall Sirdar striding up and down, brushing at his beard and swearing as he sought for words. Truly, the great Afghan was no writer of polite letters.

To the Padishah Ghazi health and long years. Between friend and friend let there be no mouthing of untrue things. His Majesty and I rode stirrup to stirrup as youths, and he knows I am his servant speaking only what is true. Was I a falcon to Akbar, and naught but

a crow to Jahangir? Have I not served the salt, unquestioning, for twoscore years? My face hath been turned
from the court, not by my own will. Now I hear that the
court and empire is ruled by the will of a wife of His
Majesty. Men of rank boast openly that they are her
servants. By God, this is astonishing and hard to believe.
Even my learned shaven heads say that never in history
was a ruler so dominated by a woman. If the fountain-
head of power becomes polluted, what shall happen to
the streams that flow from it? What will men say in the
future of the Padishah who gave her rein in this way?
A woman would make a dung cake of India and set fire
to it for her own pleasure. His Majesty is the son of
Akbar, and the Throne he sits upon is that of Timur.
Let him take the reins in his own hand and show his face
to those who serve him afar. One matter should be
looked to. By his command I ordered the hot wires to be
thrust into the eyes of Prince Khusrau. Now I beg that
he will release the blind prince from captivity in Kurram's guard. The peace of the empire and His Majesty's
safety demand that there be more than one claimant for
the Throne, after him. Look well to Khusrau's life.

A smile touched her lips as she folded the copy
away. Mahabat Khan, fierce and strident as an eagle
of his own hills, honest and direct as the steel he
wore at his side. How well she understood him, and
how amazed he would be if he knew that she had
heard all his opinions long ago, in the guise of a
youthful ahadi, sitting in the Sirdar's tent. He would
be easier to manage—although he would have
mocked one who told him so—than Jahangir, who
had hidden depths within him.

And Mahabat Khan had advised well concerning Khusrau. She knew that Jahangir had given order, the day after reading the letter, to summon the blind prince from Kurram's camp down at the foot of India. Jahangir had been cool to her for three or four days after reading this letter; then it had slipped from his mind, although not from hers. . . . Lying sleepless on the cushions, she stretched out her hand to the silk shade of the lamp, and then let it fall. What good to put out the light and stare into darkness? Her women were curled up asleep, shadows beyond the bed. Voices echoed in her ears, voices of pain that came from other women who could not sleep.

Wind-driven dust pattered against the outer cloth of the pavilion, and a cat cried near at hand. Nur Mahal raised her head, recognizing the spitting whine of a leopard. It would be Prithvi's pet, disconsolate without its mistress in the dark. The leopard went away, while the dust tapped gently near her head, and it seemed to her that hands were reaching out at her from the darkness. Hands groping toward her light, clutching at the edge of her garments, insatiate.

If she could escape from them, going away with her sick father into silence, where rows of faces were not turned toward her, and she did not need to listen to the voices . . . Prithvi had said she would live long years with empty hands, but surely they were full enough now. . . .

When the first streaks of light crept under the

canopy top, Nur Mahal slept. In the distance the leopard whined without ceasing.

It pleased her during the next few days to plan fresh feasts on a scale that surprised even Jahangir. In one evening she had all the great amirs of the lashgar to supper in an artificial garden, where hidden musicians imitated the songs of birds, and a waterfall appeared as if by magic. To forty-five of the grandees she gave dresses of honor and gifts of jewels.

She rode off with Jahangir to look upon the captured fort of Kangra—a nearly impregnable stronghold of the hills that had defied the Mogul's power until its capture not long before. And Jahangir was in high spirits. He examined slain jungle fowl— tried serving some at his table—and investigated Hindu shrines around which emaciated devotees sat with crossed legs, some holding up their arms as if made of iron, others staring into the sun. Concerning one he wrote in his memoirs:

They do not speak, and if they stand ten days and nights in one place, they do not move their feet. It was told me that one of them, a *Moti*, had lost the use of his limbs. I ordered them to bring him before me, and when he came I examined him, finding him wonderfully persistent in not moving. It came into my mind that drink might work some change in him. Accordingly I ordered them to give him many cups of *arak* of double strength. This was done, without bringing about the least change in him. He remained impassive until suddenly his senses left him, and they carried him out like a corpse. God the

boulders. From the gully bed rose the hot breath of scorched stones. On either side stretched black rock walls, and the peacock fans in the hands of the girl slaves behind them could not cool the lifeless air. Nur Mahal lay passive beside him, and he thought that her eyes appealed to him. The ivory-white of her skin almost matched the white muslin that clothed her.

Her silence led Jahangir to assert himself. "O heart of my heart," he said contentedly, "in another day we will drink the fresh mountain water. Ay, the plum trees will be in bloom beyond the pass, and thou shalt rest in Shalihmar."

She smiled up at him, with the lifting of the head and the crinkling of eyelids that always pleased him.

"Before the start, this day," he went on, "I took an omen from the book of Hafiz. And what thinkest thou I beheld beneath my finger?"

"I know not, save that it pleased my lord."

"A beautiful omen," he sighed. *"'Sweet is the spring and the juice of the grape; yet more than sweet is the voice of love.'* Is it not fitting that these words should have met my eye, when we are setting out to the gardens where the best of our hours together have passed? This journey will yield us another glimpse of paradise." He pondered, feeling that in this mood he could write a couplet that would be really fine. "Strange it seems to me that when thou art at my side, it matters not if we be in a garden spot or in this accursed abode of heat. When thou art absent I feel more pain."

Her fingers slipped into his, caressing them.

"Now," he went on playfully, "thou hast no one except Shaikhu Baba—Old Daddy. We will both mourn thy father, and that shall be another bond between us."

"Need we more? But who will take my father's place as minister?"

"What need to think of that, during our journey?"

Even after ten years of marriage he could surprise her. What need of a minister and a treasurer of the empire, for two months? Already the week's vacancy of the office during Ghias Beg's last days had disordered routine and set subordinates to quarreling. Someone was needed to take the reins of affairs at once. And Nur Mahal hoped wistfully that Jahangir, roused by the death of Ghias Beg, would select a man able to take up the burden the minister had let fall—someone who could serve Jahangir and herself as Ghias Beg had done.

But when she pressed him, he became moody and mentioned names at hazard. While she listened, she ran over in her mind the men who could fill the need —Khan Jahan Lodi, whose integrity no one questioned, but bound by blood ties to the Southern princes rather than to Jahangir; the Mota Raja, old, fat, and honorable, yet too close to the Rajputs to be safe in a crisis. If only Shaikh Farid or another of the faithful servants of Akbar had survived! She thought briefly of her brother Asaf Khan, bound by blood ties to her and Jahangir. At heart she knew him to be a coward, and outwardly he seemed intent only on magnificence. And, strangely, he had never shown any desire to succeed his father.

"If God would bestow upon me," Jahangir remarked idly, "another Persian."

No, she decided, there was no one who could be
trusted with the Diwan's seal—Jahangir being as
he was. She had hoped that a man might be found
to serve.

"There is a Persian," she responded, "already bestowed upon thee, Shaikhu Baba."

"Who?"

"Me."

For a moment he stared, wondering. "Thou,
Mihri, a woman to be Diwan of the empire?"

"I, Mihri." She laughed softly and even the listening girls did not know how much art went into the
laugh that sounded joyful. "Bethink thee, O my
heart, already thou hast made me the imperial gift
of all the possessions of Ghias Beg. If I am to have
his riches, I should not shirk his duties. Hast thou
forgotten that for years my hand was beside his in
his labor? We were poor people, raised by thy love
to rule."

When he had exclaimed against this, she explained
—casually, as if reminding him of what he knew
already—that she had no intention of working
among the officials of the Treasury, or of sitting with
the Council. The real decision lay always with the
Mogul in person, and the Diwan merely served to
carry out his wishes. The actual labor of administration lay with the subordinates such as Sadik Khan
and the *sarkars*. With the Treasury she would have
little to do, except that the seal would be in her

keeping, and vital questions would pass to her—and hence to Jahangir.

"So no other mind may come between us."

As for the Council, she would hear all discussions and decide what was insignificant without troubling Jahangir—she did not add that she did this already.

"Truly thou art my gift from God," he exclaimed. He understood perfectly what she desired. After the fellowship that had existed between himself, Nur Mahal, and Ghias Beg, she did not wish another Diwan to hold authority. Besides, he could always with a word appoint another to relieve her, and the last years had been so full of peace that the task of the new Diwan should be pleasant enough. So he reasoned, inwardly delighted. It was the same Nur Mahal who had taken her place at his side in the banquet pavilion and hunting field.

"What will Mahabat Khan think?" she smiled, at a sudden recollection of the Sirdar's heated letter.

"Eh—the Afghan? Why, he hath no love for women; but if he could once behold thy face he would love thee, as all men do."

"Nay, he hath only armies in his mind—and youthful ahadis." She looked away abruptly, and he saw her cheek curve strangely. "What is the news of Khusrau, my lord?"

"Eh—the prince? I have thought much of him and decided that he would be safer under my protection. Long since, I ordered Kurram to send him north, riding as a free son of mine on a horse, with suitable mounted attendants."

"And where is he now?"

BABAR   HUMAYUN
JAHANGIR   AKBAR

FOUR GENERATIONS OF THE GREAT MOGULS

From a contemporary tapestry

JAHANGIR AND ONE OF HIS WIVES

FROM "MINIATURE PAINTING OF PERSIA, INDIA AND TURKEY," BY F. R. MARTIN

"Why, he should be near Agra. He will come to have the honor of saluting me, of course." Jahangir moved impatiently, breathing with difficulty. "Have we not talked enough of duties? What hast thou planned for the festival on the lake, in the City of the Sun?"

V

HE lashgar climbed slowly toward the pass, buffeted now by cold winds and sudden lashings of rain. It wound past a chasm in the cliff where a cascade roared, and Jahangir paused to order the building of a pleasure palace below the waterfall. It left the elephants and plains camels behind, to go forward on horseback and in mule litters, crawling around the shoulders of mountains blasted by fire where the first mighty deodars reared from the forest mesh.

Beyond the pass appeared the fresh green slopes of Kashmir, and the breeze that caressed them came from distant snow peaks. The moving court of the Mogul entered a new world, without dust or glare, where wide oak groves stood guard beside the road.

To Nur Mahal, as to Jahangir, the fields of Kashmir brought solace. For a little, she had left India

behind, and she refused to think of anything except
the gigantic garden that lay about her. She rode at a
foot pace along a winding river where the shadows
showed violet against the ten-thousand-foot shoulder
of a mountain. The very sunlight became amber and
gold.

For a while they visited the City of the Sun,
mingling with the fair-faced Kashmiris, entering
the *dungas* of the lake—canoe-like boats manned by
small girls who wielded heart-shaped paddles—to
float out to the islands and see what changes had
been made in the gardens.

Here the sunlight did not strike into the body, as
in the lowlands. Nur Mahal liked to lie outstretched,
gazing at the cloud masses towering into the sky
above the gray mist that formed about the mountain
summits. Through the mist's veil she could see the
gleam of snow. And it was pleasant to hear the voices
of waters, the slip-slap of small waves against the
boat's side—the splash and drip of paddles.

For the night she planned water festivals, putting
lights on the imperial barges, and ordering lanterns
hung in festoons between the aspens that fringed the
islands. Then, with Jahangir, who was thoroughly
content at such a time, she could drift past the
feasters on their carpets under the lights, hearing the
songs of the boatmen, and thinking not at all.

"Thou art a spirit from Peristan," Jahangir cried
once, "asleep and hidden during the day, but alive
in the hours of darkness."

She turned to look up at him curiously. "And my
lord fears not a spirit of darkness?"

"God knows that I do not. Now this is very pleasant, and I think I will drink wine."

They bought candy from the booths along the shore, and tossed it to the throngs of children, who squealed with delight, and made no attempt to cry the monotonous, "Padishah salamet!"

While Nur Mahal watched the sacred goldfish in the temple pools, Jahangir went off on expeditions to catch water fowl in nets—for the time being he had vowed that he would kill no more animals with a gun—until he had the whim to explore the mountain slopes.

Then they went up with a few servants, since no enemies were to be guarded against in this strange quiet land, beyond the gypsies and cattle of the high pastures, to the depths of the deodars, where the drooping fringe of the forest giants made a twilight about them, and they could look down upon the silver, winding river.

Still higher they climbed, to sit at night about fires in the hush of the upper air, to watch the moon rise —to see the white glow touch snow peaks and glaciers, one after the other. They discussed the stars, some men saying the pure air made the star-gleam brighter here than over the plains below, others saying that this was the home of the gods.

And Nur Mahal wondered if the hills of Khorassan that she had never seen were like these mountains.

The air of the higher altitudes troubled Jahangir, who enjoyed most the visits to Shalihmar. He had spared no exertions to make this one spot just what his fancy demanded. From the river a stone-bordered canal led between rows of poplars to a pleasure palace surrounded by fountains and by smaller kiosks.

Sitting in the open balconies of the palace he could gaze down the canal, with its fairy-like bridges and play of fountains under the dark arch of the poplars, to the blue of the lake itself. On the gilt wall above him was an inscription in Persian:

"If there be a Paradise on earth, it is this, it is this."

He was at Shalihmar one day with a few musicians, experimenting with the sound of flutes and guitars played over the water, and Nur Mahal was resting in her pavilion beside the canal before dressing for the supper they were to have in the water palace, when she received the first word of Khusrau.

A courier from India had sought her in the city, and now waited in the anteroom, caked with dust and trembling with fatigue. He would not give his message to her secretaries, but sent in a ring to her. She recognized it as the signet of Fedai Khan, a companion of the blind prince in the Dekkan, and went to sit behind the silk curtain that screened her from visitors. The courier pressed his head to the carpet, whispering:

"O Most Imperial, the word is from the lips of Fedai Khan to thine ear. Khusrau is dead in the camp of Prince Kurram."

She caught her breath. "In what way?"

"The physicians say he died of stomach pains.

Fedai Khan, his friend, says that he was strangled.
At the time Kurram was absent, hunting. That night
Reza, a slave of Kurram's tents, entered the room of
the blind prince and left again in a little. Nothing
more is known, but the prince was not dangerously
ill, and a skillful strangler leaves no clear mark upon
a body."

Nur Mahal thought of the order that had gone to
Kurram, to deliver the blind prince to his father.
"There is no proof?"

"No proof, O Most Imperial. Yet the physicians
and courtiers who signed the statement that Khusrau
died of a stomach ailment did not visit him that
night. They saw only the body."

"Thou hast leave to go. At my door they will give
thee gold and anything thou hast need of."

She dismissed the man absently, her thoughts playing about that room a thousand miles distant. Kurram had murdered his brother. He had received the
order, his slave had been seen to enter the room when
the prince was alone—the blind were too often alone
—and surely Kurram had not gone hunting that
night by chance. But there would be no particle of
evidence, except the signed certificate declaring that
Khusrau had died of sickness. By now the slave Reza
would be removed from sight, probably slain.

While her maids combed back and anointed her
hair—she could not be late for the sitting down to
supper in Shalihmar—she pondered the situation.
She had no illusions whatever, and instinct told her
that Kurram, the heir, had struck a blow at Jahangir
and herself by eliminating the blind Khusrau. It was

murder, carefully thought out and deftly executed at just the right moment for Kurram.

The lives of the Moguls had been violent enough before then. Once Akbar, maddened by overfatigue and spirits, had tried to dash his body against a sword fixed in the stones of a wall. More than once she had heard Jahangir quote the proverb, "Kingship hath no kinship." But she knew that Jahangir cherished a real love for the blind prince—feeling more drawn to him than to the cold and always successful Kurram. So long as Khusrau lived, Kurram dared not draw the sword against his father, who was growing weaker yearly. To have done so would have been to throw Khusrau's partisans on the side of the imperial court.

Now Kurram had simply removed Khusrau from the field. And Nur Mahal felt the chill of horror when she thought of the blind man, put to death in silence while under Kurram's protection. If only the last illness of her father had not turned her eyes for a moment from the Dekkan! If only she had been quick enough to warn Khusrau secretly, instead of waiting for Jahangir to act! She was faced, before Ghias Beg had been placed in his tomb, with rebellion as certain as the darkness now closing in upon the pine-shadowed camp. "The silver diadem," she instructed her maids absently, "with the glass bangles. I will have the rope of pink pearls—no other jewels."

She considered Kurram's point of view dispassionately. The great prince had been making allies instead of making war in the Dekkan, by cementing friendship with one chieftain after the other in the south, and in the always unsettled Malwa and Bengal. So much her spies had assured her—explaining that Kurram appeared only to be bringing in the southern princes to allegiance to the Mogul. Thus, he could command his own army, the pick of the Mogul's hosts, and the powers of the extreme south. In armed strength he was now Jahangir's equal—as a leader he would be much more capable. . . . What would be his next act?

Impatiently she slipped on her bracelets, and looked to make certain that her hair was right before shrouding herself in the light head veil. Jahangir always noticed the slight details of her attire.

Why, in Kurram's place she would do nothing openly. He had struck his blow and made time his ally. Now he would wait, to see whether Jahangir would dare march down the length of India against him . . . which would be a mistake on the Mogul's part . . . or whether Jahangir would decide to take no measures against him, which would be worse. The eyes of India would be watching to see whether the Mogul felt himself too weak to punish his son. . . .

"Most Imperial," a maid whispered, "our lord hath seated himself at the cloth."

Swiftly Nur Mahal rose and made her way to the canal and the waiting barge. In the square chamber of the water palace Jahangir sat munching sugared ginger, surrounded by smiling Kashmiri girls, unveiled, and some older poets and musicians.

"Thou hast added the ache of hunger to the pain

of too-long separation," he reproached her. "I have it in my mind to make trial of the flesh of roasted duck of a new brown species, with wine sauce."

When she murmured a response and took her place, the gleam of the gold inscription overhead caught her eye, and she repeated the words:

" 'If there be a Paradise on earth, this is it, this is it.' "

With sincere admiration Jahangir turned to her. "Why is it, O delight of my heart, that thou canst always find the most apt words for any occasion?"

Many days passed before Jahangir was informed publicly of the death of his son, and it became apparent to Nur Mahal that he meant to take no action at all. He read over the signed statement himself, making no secret of his grief, yet he said nothing to her. In his memoirs he wrote:

At this time a report came from Kurram that Khusrau had died of colic pains and gone to the mercy of God. Previously, my huntsmen and servants had been ordered to make ready a hunting circuit in the game preserve of Girjhak. When I went out to hunt with some special companions, we took one hundred and twenty-four head of rams and antelope.

"Kurram's honor was at stake for the life of thy blind son," she reminded him. "More than a month had passed since he had thine order to send Khusrau hither. He did not obey the order."

"Perhaps little Khusrau was too ill to travel."

"Yet no word was sent thee of his illness! And what proof is there of the manner of his death?"

"The oath of honorable men."

"Who are loyal to Kurram. Wilt thou not order them to appear in the Presence to swear to what they signed?"

For a moment he considered. "God alone knows all secrets. It was Khusrau's kismet that he should die, and what is to be gained by prolonging the pain of his death?"

Nur Mahal had to set her lip between her teeth to keep from answering. What was to be gained! She could have wept at Jahangir's lassitude. Yet how well she understood his point of view. With Khusrau gone, he had only two sons by legitimate wives, and of the two Parviz the elder was a hard drinking fool. Kurram called him *Neh shudani*—Good-for-Naught—truthfully. Kurram was still his father's idol, the leader of his armies, the prop of the empire. If he brought accusation of murder against Kurram, publicly and without actual proof, he would antagonize his proud and utterly ambitious son. Undoubtedly he suspected that Kurram had ordered the murder of the blind prince, but he knew nothing for certain. And he chose, now that the harm was done, to let the question pass.

Useless for her to argue against his decision. Jahangir believed implicitly in his own God-given power to rule. If he wished to ignore his son's crime, his wish was final. She could influence Jahangir in everything, except his own conduct and his treatment of his sons. So she searched for something else to move him, and found it in fresh news from the border.

The first inkling of it was a terse message from Mahabat Khan. "The tribes are gathering and slaying merchants more than usual. They have been stirred up to fighting."

Pillage was nothing new in the Afghan hills; but the Mogul's commanders had their hands full just now with serious attacks. There followed a warning from Khan Jahan Lodi, governor of Multan, near the hills. The army of the Shah of Persia had advanced to the western frontier stronghold of Kandahar and was laying siege to it.

Kandahar, Nur Mahal knew, had been a bone of contention between the Moguls and their powerful neighbors, the great Shahs. But the Persians had managed to deceive Jahangir with elaborate embassies of good-will, until their army could be moved secretly to the walls of Kandahar. Unprepared and ill garrisoned, it fell after a short siege. To the certainty of coming rebellion, was added invasion on the western frontier.

The danger from Kandahar became more urgent when Jahangir, roused by the prospect of battle, announced that he himself would lead an army to recapture the city, to invade Persia, and lay in waste the Shah's city of Isfahan.

Nur Mahal made no effort to dissuade him, although she was quite well aware that they had no forces available for such an expedition—that if the lashgar departed on such a march, it would meet inevitable disaster in the desert borderland and would leave its rear and all India open to Kurram. "Ay, Shah Abbas hath struck thy hand of friendship with the knife of treachery," she assented, "and surely his agents persuaded the tribes to rise against thy standard."

She let his anger run its course, while the lashgar journeyed back over the passes into India, and Jahangir debated daily with his council—until he began to be weary of details of mobilization. He had sent couriers throughout the north, ordering levies of troops and strings of elephants, parks of artillery to be assembled in Multan, on the road to Kandahar. In all this Nur Mahal aided him diligently, even suggesting that the imperial treasures in Delhi and Agra be moved north. Jahangir was delighted with the prospect of the grand army to be assembled.

"But who is to command it?" she wondered, and gave no sign that this was the point she had foreseen from the first. "There is only one who should lift thy standard—Kurram, the Ever Victorious."

"Ay, Kurram."

"Then send for him. It is time. Order him to hasten to thee, at Multan or Lahore."

"With how much of his army? All his forces cannot leave the Dekkan."

"Let him decide what to bring and what to leave in the south. Is he not able to decide?"

So the order went to Kurram, with all the speed of hard-ridden horses, and Nur Mahal waited expectantly. Without Jahangir's perceiving it, she had placed the prince in a dilemma. Kurram, knowing that the guilt of Khusrau's blood lay upon him, could

not know what Jahangir intended toward him. If
Kurram obeyed his father's command—and in time
of war he must obey or proclaim himself a rebel—
and hastened north alone, he would place himself
utterly in Jahangir's power. Nur Mahal fancied
that he did not fear Jahangir's wrath so much as her
own enmity. If he abandoned the Dekkan and
brought all his army up to the mobilization, he
would find Jahangir with an equal army equipped
for battle. In either case, if he consented to lead an
expedition into the Afghan hills, he would leave his
supporters in India scattered and open to persuasion
or force, perhaps for years.

To pave the way for Kurram's journey, Nur
Mahal induced Jahangir to have Khusrau's body
brought to Agra. So, before the murderer, the funeral cortège of the blind prince traveled slowly, and
at each halting place—for the common people had
loved Khusrau—gathered devotees who mourned
and built shines where the body had rested. Through
the multitudes ran the message that the blind man
had been a saint and that affliction could be healed
at his shrines. Only Nur Mahal had pondered the
effect of this upon Kurram, who must come over the
same road. It was a woman's blow, but it struck
home.

Kurram hesitated, and made his first mistake by
an attempt to negotiate. He sent a letter explaining
his willingness to take command of the Mogul army,
but demanding that the army should be under his
sole command, and with it all the cities and garrisons of the northwest. Only too well he saw the use-

lessness of an attempt to invade Persia, and sought to transfer his military control from the south to the northwest. He added that he was on the road but could only arrive after the rains.

Shrewdly, he had tried to provide against the retribution of Nur Mahal's wit. But she weighed his message with a single reading and made no comment. She had guessed Jahangir's inevitable response.

The Mogul had been sincerely roused by the blow at Kandahar, and now in what he felt to be his hour of need, he found Kurram bargaining with him arrogantly. He responded at once, and in plain words —since Kurram meant to delay until after the rains, the prince must send immediately to the royal standard all his officers, the Sayyids of Barha, the Shaikhzadas, the Afghan and Rajput cavalry—the backbone of his army.

Kurram did not obey. Instead he sent a spokesman north, an eloquent soul who harangued Jahangir very ably—demanding for Kurram an explanation of why Jahangir had turned against him, reproaching the Mogul for being governed by a woman, and asking plaintively what Kurram was to do, while Nur Mahal, his antagonist, reigned at court. Was he to abandon his lands and people and become an ascetic, or go on pilgrimage to Mecca?

And from behind the curtain Nur Mahal listened, unsmiling, weighing the effect of the exhortation upon the stout, heavily breathing man who sat on the throne. If she had taken an open stand against Kurram weeks before in Kashmir, Jahangir might have been moved by Kurram's emissary. As it was, she had let Kurram walk into a trap of his own making, and Jahangir could not forgive disobedience on the part of a prince at the head of an army. Impatiently he dismissed the envoy without a reply and with only a formal present. That night he complained to her naïvely.

"Surely God must have afflicted Kurram with madness. What is to be done with him?"

"He makes pretense to be faithful to thee, Old Daddy," she replied casually; "if he is, surely he will not march against thee, but will return to his own estates in the Dekkan."

And Jahangir wrote in his memoirs:

I ordered Kurram to go back to his own *jagir* and not to set his foot outside it, and to send to me all the servants of the empire under his orders. If he does not, I shall call him Bi-daulat—Rebel.

Then couriers brought to the court the final response of the prince. He had mustered his followers for war, and was advancing north, hoping to catch his father the emperor unprepared. With him marched a no less able general, Raja Bikramajit, and the Dekkan princes.

The news seemed to stupefy Jahangir, already wearied by the preparations for war and the journey over the pass to the first towns of India. He drank steadily, and roused only at the prospect of hunting. To those who tried to draw his attention to his danger he responded:

"Nur Mahal is the one who is able to rule. A little meat and a little wine will content me."

He even abandoned his memoirs, writing down, with characteristic analysis of his own feelings:

As a result of the weakness that began two years ago, my heart and my brain do not work in accord. I cannot make notes of events as formerly.

Under Nur Mahal's urging he consented to keep moving toward Agra. But he was incapable of assembling an army, much less leading one. She sent orders to all the supporters of the emperor in the North to unite at Lahore. And she signed herself a dispatch to Mahabat Khan, bidding the Afghan take command of the new Mogul army. He alone would be able to lead fresh levies against the disciplined forces of Kurram and Bikramajit—who were already within sight of Ajmere. Meanwhile she sent Prince Shahriyar toward the Afghan border, with the skeleton of an army to make a feint toward Kandahar.

The Khan's response came back at once, and she felt the chill of fear at her heart as she read it.

"Am I a dog, to be sent from the court for ten years, and then bidden to return? There are too many traitors in the court, and I will not share bread and salt with traitors."

For a moment she sat gazing blankly at the roll of rice paper with the bold words traced across it. The Sirdar could not have been won over to Kurram's side; his loyalty was beyond question. His anger must have been roused by stories he had heard of her

JAHANGIR WITH THE PORTRAIT OF AKBAR

FROM "MINIATURE PAINTING OF PERSIA, INDIA AND TURKEY," BY F. R. MARTIN

MOGUL'S SON RIDING TO THE HUNT

BLOCHET—PEINTURES DE MANUSCRITS ARABES, PERSAN ET TURCS
DE LA BIBLIOTHÈQUE NATIONALE

dominance—she remembered his opinion about women, and his letter to Jahangir.

After a little, she wrote a second missive—not a command but a challenge as brief as his own.

"Is Mahabat Khan false to the Mogul's salt that he has eaten? At this time the army of rebellion moves toward Fathpur. If the Sirdar will not take command, I, Nur Mahal, shall do so."

It was carried to the hills with the speed of desperation. While she waited, she heard almost hourly tidings from the capital, reports that the rebels were within sight of Fathpur's red walls—that Raja Bikramajit was on the way to raid Agra. Then, instead of a letter, a Pathan trooper arrived at the lashgar to say to her attendants that Mahabat Khan was close behind him, and would reach the lashgar that evening.

"At what hour?" Nur Mahal demanded.

The Pathan thought it would be about moonrise, but it might be at the first star-gleam, because the Sirdar rode as if Satan were at his tail.

That afternoon heavy clouds raced across a red sunset, and on the heels of a wind that sent dust whirling over the pavilions rain came down in gusts. In the gathering darkness the lashgar, always tumultuous at the evening meal, became a limbo of sound and confusion. Through it Nur Mahal picked her way as best she could.

This time Arslan did not accompany her. She had left the Turk, in spite of his remonstrance, at the *khanate* gate, and had gone on alone, riding a nondescript horse, with a dark fur wrap pulled over her shoulders and head.

Clouds of heavy smoke from the dung fires swirled around her, choking her. Strings of laden camels coming in late blocked the avenues of the great camp, and when she turned aside she found herself in a network of tent ropes and bales. The few cleared places had been preëmpted by men who had lost themselves in the confusion and were setting up their tents haphazard to escape the rain.

"Khabar dar! Khabar dar!"

The cry of the watchmen, who wielded long bamboo staves against the shoulders and heads of hapless wanderers, sounded like the barking of dogs. Someone screamed, and a chorus of guttural curses answered, until the splintering fall of bazaar booths drowned it all. A savage elephant might have escaped from the lines, or some amir with his horsemen was taking the shortest way to his quarters regardless of the crowds or tent shelters in his way.

The lashgar had grown disorderly during the march down from Kashmir. It seemed to Nur Mahal as if the collapse of the Mogul had affected the officers, who had lost their grip upon the throngs under them, and the uncertainty of the men had maddened the animals. That, and the rain, and the quarreling. More than once she had to turn back before drawn swords, and it was only a fortunate glimpse of the towering Sky Lamp that enabled her to find the main avenue and gallop beyond the tents to the river's edge. She saw no guards posted—only bands of stragglers hurrying in to escape being looted.

The lashgar had been pitched on the near bank of the river Jhelum, and a path led a mile or so to the sandy ford. When she reached it she found herself in a nest of hillocks and scrub, rustling under the buffeting of the wind. To escape notice—for a woman alone outside the lines of the lashgar would arouse instant curiosity—she dismounted and led the horse to the edge of the brush.

But few people were coming over the ford from the west. Mahabat Khan would come that way, she knew, and she stared at every band of riders. She was shivering under the fur, but not from the cold.

Nur Mahal understood clearly what was happening. Prince Kurram and the rebels had decided to risk open war with the weakening Jahangir, and now only armed force could turn back the tide of rebellion. There were men enough, perhaps loyal enough, in the north to make a stand against Kurram. But in some way unknown to her they had been scattered and misinformed. The very guards of the lashgar did not realize what was happening. The officials around Jahangir were unable to get together the nucleus of an army, and a strong hand was needed to take command at once. A month more, and Kurram might be master of Agra.

Mahabat Khan was her only hope. The Sirdar was worshiped by the Rajputs and feared by the Afghans. The other princes had faith in his leadership, and the very sight of him in the lashgar would restore confidence. She did not dare think what would happen if he took offense and went over to the apparently victorious rebels. And now, if that Pa-

than had told the truth, he would be riding down to
this ford in no pleasant mood. She had her own letter
to thank for that. Under her hood Nur Mahal
laughed softly to herself. At least he was coming.

She had plenty of time to realize how slight was
the chance at which she snatched, before a torch
flared on the far bank, and hoofs thudded through
the mud. A score of men in gray felt *burkas,* soaked
and streaked with mud, were galloping down to the
sand bar. They reined in, splashing through the
water, and Nur Mahal heard them talking in the
harsh Pashtu of the hills. They pointed to the gleam
of the Sky Lamp in the distance.

Climbing back into her saddle, shivering at touch
of the wet leather, she urged her horse across the
path. The troopers peered at her, astonished, and a
voice from the cavalcade mocked her:

"Are there not whores enough in the Shaitan-
khanah, that thou shouldst come to drive trade at the
ford?"

Mahabat Khan—she could see his black beard
under the close-drawn hood—was riding past, when
she called his name. But not the name known in
India.

"O son of Ghiyar Beg!"

He reined in sharply, his horse rocketing toward
her. "What manner of begging is this?"

"I was sent, O Sirdar," she responded swiftly, "by
the Light of the Palace, with word for——"

"With Nur Mahal I may talk, but not with her
maid."

He had turned away impatiently, when she called

after him. "You were not in such haste to leave me at the Bihar serai when the talk was of the treachery of Malik Ambar, and you tossed dice with the mullah."

A chance memory of years before, when she had wandered in the disguise of a trooper, but Mahabat Khan, it seemed, also remembered it—while an amir behind him swore that here was a faithful love indeed. Mahabat Khan curtly ordered his men to divide and to ride before and behind him out of hearing. When Nur Mahal was trotting at his side, he remarked that she must be a witch. "If thou hast a message, tell it in plain words. I have no time for Persian trickery."

A ripple of laughter answered him. "I am Nur Mahal, but I have no mind to trick thee, now."

"Thou!" The Afghan shook his head. "Am I a Jat buffalo driver to believe such talk?"

"O Sirdar, you asked for plain words, saying that you would speak with Nur Mahal but not with her maid. I have ventured hither because the Padishah, my lord, hath dire need of thee."

The clear voice startled the old Afghan, and he peered at her sidewise, half convinced. "What need to come here? I have heard that you—the princess talks with strange men through the curtain at will."

"Ay, and many ears listen. There are spies in the harem and traitors in the lashgar. Look!" She stretched her hand out of her sleeve, holding it near to his eyes so that he could recognize the signet ring. "Waste no more moments in doubt, Sirdar. Tomorrow you may speak with me in court through the curtain and know for certain that I am Nur Mahal."

He ran his fingers through his beard and swore. "By Allah, has madness afflicted you?"

"Nay, son of Ghiyar Beg, but great need. Hast thou forgotten that Nur Mahal was once daughter of Ghias Beg in thy city of Kabul—often kicking her heels against the garden wall and watching thee ride past? I am of the hills as thou art, born upon the desert road as thou wast not, and accustomed to the saddle, as thou seest. Let there be no talk of Persian trickery between us in this hour of calamity."

Swiftly, knowing that he could not listen without the certainty that she was Nur Mahal, she explained the murder of Khusrau, the defiance sent Jahangir by Kurram, the advance of the rebel army. She told him frankly that Jahangir had lost his capacity to assume the leadership, and warned him that treachery as well as inefficiency had kept the Mogul's followers from uniting.

"Never had king such need of a sword-hand as my lord hath need of you," she said softly.

He listened intently, slowing to a walk, and glancing at her veiled head. Apparently he accepted her as Nur Mahal, but she felt that he was still on his guard—almost incredulous that the favorite of the Mogul could meet him at a river ford. "Ay," he muttered, "when the hunt is on, the hound is called out of his corner and fed. For the best of my life I have been no more than an exile, with the pay of a common mansabdar. By the eyes of God, the gifts I sent to court were the spoil I took from my enemies with this hand." He flung his open palm out, and his fingers clenched with a cracking of bones. "Other riches had I not, yet the grandees of the court had gold upon their palace walls. Was that a little thing? It is true. To Jahangir I would give the blood of my body, but, by the eyes of God, I will not come at call to those who have lived off the leavings from his table. Let them die."

Nur Mahal flung up her head. "Would I be here at hazard of my life—as thou hast seen, this little while—if I served not my lord faithfully, as thou hast done?"

In silence he rode a bit, unwilling to admit it, yet too honest to deny it.

"Because I cannot talk to them in the open," she went on bitterly, "men can whisper what comes into their heads of me, and who is to deny? Know I not the treachery of the court? Ask my people how often they have found poison in my dishes. Sirdar, with a word spoken yonder—" she pointed to the lofty Sky Lamp—"you can disgrace Nur Mahal. I came on no greater surety than trust in you. And you speak to me of treachery. Have I not cause to know it more than thee? Live for a month at the harem gate, and learn what treachery can be."

"Highness," he said, and reined in his horse. Suddenly he nodded, and spoke with assurance. "Good, I believe that we twain serve the salt truly. What others be there fit to command near the Padishah?"

"Khwaja Abu'l Hasan."

"An old fox, but never of one mind. Who else?"

"Abdullah Khan——"

"Who would sell his mother's flesh for silver."

"I did not think so. My brother, Asaf Khan."

"Who would leave the army to ride to a banquet. He can do more harm than a traitor. If you wish me to serve, give me command over the first two and send your brother away—anywhere."

Nur Mahal remembered that the old Sirdar had quarreled with Asaf, who had been careful to keep him on the border thereafter. "Be it so. Asaf Khan shall depart tonight to look after the Agra treasure."

The Afghan grunted, rubbing the end of his whip through his horse's mane. She had spoken too quickly, and he, unaccustomed to the rapid play of her woman's mind, thought that she had thrown him a promise as she would toss meat to a hunting dog. "Asaf Khan is commander of twelve thousand horsemen, and is also Master of the Household with his own battle standard and escort of drums. Will he go off now, at this moment? He may consent with words, but will he leave his men?"

For a moment she pondered, realizing that this soldier who had passed his years in the camps was aware of difficulties unforeseen by her—who had dealt with the ever shifting kaleidoscope of intrigue within the court. Still, she felt that she understood her amiable brother. Asaf Khan would obey her, and he would go far to escape a battle.

"Tomorrow," she said slowly, "when you have your audience, O Mahabat Khan, my brother shall be appointed governor of Bengal. But his cavalry contingent must be left with the army."

This was a clear promise, and the Afghan muttered approval. "Kurram has the only army," he responded grimly. "The Sayyids of Barha are with his standard. Bikramajit, who stormed Kangra and subdued the Dekkan, is at his side. By Allah, I think that raja is the spirit of the revolt. . . . He hath won over Kunwar Bhim with the horsemen of Mewar—the best men who ever climbed into saddle."

"Yet only a blind man," she objected at once, "would believe Kurram hath an army. You know, as I do, that it comes forward like a wolf pack, ready to spring or to draw back. It hath two hearts. Bikramajit is all for the war; he hath set his foot too far to draw back. And those wild boys Udai Ram and Kunwar Bhim will fight to the last. But the heart of that army—thou knowest the word for the core of a Mogul host since the day of Timur?— is undecided. The cavalry guards have eaten the Mogul's salt too long not to feel shame. They come forward as rebels, with their faces blackened. A message from thee to their leaders——"

"Ay, true." He caught her thought. "They would listen to one who spoke for the Padishah. Tell me what forces are ready to join the imperial standard?"

A blunt question that Mahabat Khan might have flung at the treasurer of the army. Nur Mahal, however, had labored for weeks in coercing and rallying just those contingents, and he listened with growing surprise while she ran off numbers and positions— adding the condition of their horses and the time it would take them to reach Lahore, now the center of mobilization.

"Ay," he nodded, brushing up his beard with

new conviction, "ay, Fedai Khan is worth two regiments . . . and Prince Parviz comes with six thousand . . . the gathering place is well chosen . . . but who persuaded thee not to wait for the artillery?"

"It is always too late," she explained. "Like the elephants, which are better with the lashgar. Once you yourself said that the first battle of a war is decided by cavalry alone, and I have not forgotten."

In spite of himself Mahabat Khan smiled. "By the breath of God, a good commander was lost in thee." A last doubt assailed him. "Your Highness will not try to interfere with the forces under my command?"

"If you knew what I have already upon my head!" Her laugh, half hysterical, caught in a sob, and she put her hand on his arm. "From the moment you set your foot in the stirrup, O son of Ghiyar Beg, your authority will be above any other."

She saw him nod again, and knew that she had won his loyalty, if not his formal consent, which he would give only to Jahangir. "Take me to my quarters," she urged.

Mahabat Khan ceased pondering matters of state to assume command of his small detachment. At a word from him, the Afghan amirs cast away their felt cloaks and appeared in khalats of silk and leather, and in silvered chain mail. They closed up around her, struck into a gallop, and, with the Sirdar riding before them in his familiar white satin coat and small gray *pagri* a little aslant, they passed the outer gateway like an eddy of wind and headed into

the confusion of the main avenue. The throngs gave
way before them, and Nur Mahal listened expectantly. She had been at some pains to make certain the
Afghan's arrival would be noticed.

"Mahabat Khan!" voices cried out. "The Sirdar
comes. . . . Hah, fortunate is this hour!"

Above the cries resounded the clamor of the great
kettledrums at the gate of the imperial enclosure.
And as the Afghans drew rein, surprised, the
mounted guard formed hastily in two lines, clearing
the way to the gate—as if greeting a visiting prince.
The officer of the guard came out with drawn scimitar, while his men jostled and edged forward for a
sight of the distinguished general, their swords making play against their shields. Nur Mahal, accustomed to the disorder of the military part of the
camp, saw nothing amiss in this, but Mahabat Khan
ordered his detachment to halt.

"Shikar Beg," he called crisply to the young commander of the guard, "when thou wert a brat running about my horse's tail I thought thou didst know
somewhat of horses and drill. Hast thou been licking
the cup, or straddling a wench—to sit the saddle in
this fashion?"

The face of Shikar Beg flushed in the glare of the
Sky Lamp, but before he could speak, the Afghan
looked wonderingly down the two wavering lines—
the men had been crowding forward to hear more of
what he might say to the young noble. "Have all the
men fit to hold a sword," he cried at them, "gone off
to the army, that the Mogul's guard must be formed

of cattle boys? Who gave them leave to mount chargers bearing the royal brand?"

Silence greeted his words, but in the silence the angry horsemen stiffened their backs, the scimitars crept higher upon their shoulders, the horses were reined back sharply into line, and when the Sirdar, paying no more heed to their commander, passed between them, they gazed squarely into his eyes.

"Dismount!" he bade them. "Go back to your tents and dice. By the splendor of Allah, I have not come thirty leagues between the rising and the setting of the sun to watch such play as this!"

It was a strange scene to Nur Mahal. Shikar Beg, she knew, would have made a blood feud out of such words from another leader. Yet he seemed more ashamed than sullen, and she heard a bearded Pathan trooper mutter as he led his charger away. "On my soul, this at least is a man."

There were throngs of the palace attendants to greet Mahabat Khan within the enclosure. He paid no attention to them, waiting instead until she had come up. She wondered if he would dismount to hold her stirrup, or try to safeguard her incognita by ignoring her. But he sat motionless, waiting for her to act, and she realized that he was putting her to a test before this crowd.

"By command of the Princess Nur Mahal, these quarters have been prepared for the Sirdar," she said to him, and led the way to scarlet pavilions pitched between Jahangir's and her own.

"Then render my gratitude to the Most Imperial," he said, dismounting and turning away. Arslan has-

tened forward, to take her rein while she slipped into
the shadows between the tents.

Nur Mahal had done what she could to bind the
Sirdar to Jahangir in the ride from the ford. She
could not rest, however. Her own people must be
stationed in a cordon about his quarters, to try to
prevent spies of the other side reaching him before
the morrow's audience. There were dispatches
brought in by couriers awaiting her in the Privy
Council, and Jahangir, who had been made uneasy
by her long absence, must be visited at once. While
she changed from her wet garment into silk sari and
embroidered khalat, she asked her maids what he
had found to interest him that evening.

"He hath ordered the making of a new wine cup,"
she was told, "and complains that you delay in reading to him the Book of Kings by Firdawsi. He is in
the mood to hear an account of battles."

Hastily she touched her chin and throat with the
attar of rose perfume and took up the large manuscript of Firdawsi, while the women veiled her, and
the eunuchs came to escort her across the canopied
path to the door of her husband.

The next morning Jahangir received Mahabat
Khan in public audience, after having announced
that Asaf Khan would be honored by the government of Bengal. The Mogul welcomed the Afghan
general warmly, and by a word increased his rank
and pay to eleven thousand horse. From the status
of an officer, he was raised to that of a grandee of
the empire, the equal—Nur Mahal had thought this

out with some care, and had persuaded Jahangir to
it with discreet urgency—of Asaf Khan.

Astonished and openly delighted, the Sirdar accepted the command of the army. Both Abdullah
Khan and the stately Khwaja hastened forward to
salute him.

"Art thou content, O son of Ghiyar Beg?" Nur
Mahal asked him when he stood before her curtain.
"And was not truth spoken in the rain, at the ford?"

"Ay, I am well content," he admitted, "so long as
no one from the Throne turns against me."

But she had no intention of meddling with a commander in the field. Once Mahabat Khan had taken
the responsibility, she almost wept with relief, and
watched events eagerly.

There was a week of anxiety when her unseen
enemies sent some cleverly forged reports from the
new army, attacking the officers Mahabat Khan had
promoted to command. Nur Mahal saw through the
clumsy effort at once, and had no great trouble con-
vincing Jahangir that the letters were intended to
cast suspicion upon loyal officers. Jahangir himself
caused her some difficulty. Now that he saw a loyal
army actually forming under such a man as Mahabat
Khan, he recovered his spirits—sent daily gifts of
swords, treasure, and robes of honor to his new officers, and insisted that the imperial lashgar follow
close upon the heels of Mahabat Khan. He even sent
his own war quiver, as a mark of supreme favor to
Abdullah Khan, leader of the advance. Yet it suited

Nur Mahal to have him once more in the public eye
—to outward seeming once more the Mogul, son of
Akbar.

During February of that year, 1623, the court
moved by easy stages down the great trunk road
from Lahore toward Agra, while Mahabat Khan
and Kurram, with their great armies, felt for each
other in the Agra plain.

Late in March the inevitable battle began, and the
first tidings by courier from the scene shocked her
into wild anxiety.

*"Abdullah Khan, with the ten thousand cavalry of
the advance, pretending to charge, has gone over to
the enemy."*

Hours passed before any other word came, and
Jahangir was in a fever of unrest, cursing the traitors,
and praying for a miracle that would give at least
safety to the imperial forces, now outnumbered
nearly two to one. "Let that wretch Abdullah Khan
be known hereafter as La nat 'illah," he ordered, "the
Accursed of God. Never mention him by another
name to me."

But Nur Mahal knew that abler minds than the
Khan's had plotted against her, and she reminded
Jahangir that they had not yet heard from Mahabat
Khan.

It was near midnight when an Afghan officer
lashed a sobbing horse through the gate and whipped
aside those who ran to help him from the saddle,
until he reached the entrance of the imperial tent.
He made his way to the carpet on which Jahangir

sat with his officers. Flinging himself down, he
pressed his forehead to the carpet and cried for all
to hear:

"Thus says Mahabat Khan: We have won."

Only after days did Nur Mahal realize how de-
cisive the victory had been. Bikramajit was slain, and
Kurram's forces scattered in retreat while the Sirdar's cavalry pursued. Thousands of Abdullah
Khan's men had rejoined the imperial ranks, with
the Sayyids of Barha, who had held aloof from the
fighting. Had it not been for the Mewar Rajputs,
Kurram himself might have been cut off and captured. Now he was heading for the river that marked
the boundary of his own Dekkan region in the south.

Jahangir lived in a transport of joy, sending artillery and elephants recklessly after his onrushing
army, and rewarding all loyal officers with fortunes
in precious stones. To Mahabat Khan he dispatched
a white horse-tail standard—the standard of a
Mogul's host since the time of Genghis Khan—and
imperial kettledrums. He examined carefully the
head of Raja Bikramajit that had been sent to him,
pointing out that someone had cut off the ears to
obtain the pearls in them. And he dictated a new
chapter of his memoirs to a secretary.

What shall I say of my own pains? Very weak, I must
still ride after my faithless son, through a warm country
dangerous to my health. I must put off recapturing Kandahar, yet I trust that God will remove these afflictions
from me. I gave to Mahabat Khan the title of Khan of
Khans. As for that rebel, who had a father like me, who

am verily his creator upon earth—after being denied
nothing and raised to the greatest dignity, may God
never hold him again in favor.

Nur Mahal, who had been observing her husband
curiously, made a suggestion to him that pleased him
greatly. "Old Daddy," she pleaded, "since all these
servants have been honored by your generosity, can
I not have the standard and the drums that once belonged to my father?"

"You shall have them, Mihri," he promised. "A
woman has naught to do with war, but surely you
possess the courage of a man. Now that we are at war
in this fashion, you shall have your own troops and
horse-tail standard."

The civil war did not end for three years. During
those three years, with Prince Kurram a rebel and
fugitive, with Mahabat Khan and Prince Parviz in
the field, and Asaf in Bengal, the supremacy of India
came into the hands of Nur Mahal.

VI

THEY say that Nur Mahal was never more lovely
than during those years. Perhaps this was because she appeared in public so often that her
slim white figure became the center of court life. She
wore a face veil, of course, but men looked without
hindrance into her eyes.

At times when Jahangir was too ill to be seen, she
sat alone in the jharoka window, above the multitude
that came to see their sovereign and to hand petitions
to the guards, to be placed in the hand of Nur Mahal.

When it was discovered that the imperial princess
could be more merciful than any official of the
Mogul's court, the petitions increased surprisingly.
Women, who could not have shown themselves to the
Mogul, waited for hours to approach Nur Mahal's
palanquin and attract her attention with a cry of distress or an outthrust petition.

Ambar, her head eunuch, had ceased to worry about breaking pardah. His mistress, by some miracle of Allah's intending, had become a veiled empress, a thing unknown hitherto in the lands of Islam. Now that she herself made the laws, who was to accuse her of breaking them? Ambar swelled with importance when he rode out on his caparisoned mule, his stout figure swathed in scarlet brocade and the new purple velvet that the Portuguese dogs brought from Europe.

"Is not the way made smooth?" he asked Dai Dilaram, the aged nurse of the empress. "How goes the saying—'If the Friend is willing, the task is easy'?"

"Ay," muttered Dilaram, who had her share of superstition, "it is very well to be devout as a priest, now that thy days are fat with ease. Only, don't put thy foot beyond the edge of thy sleeping carpet."

The nurse had been given the title of Ruler of Women, which pleased her mightily, even if it meant little, and her hours were filled with watching over the orphan girls who came in growing crowds to Agra's citadel.

"Eh, only a fool complains when his cup is full to running over," Ambar retorted. Being a man of affairs, he considered himself wiser than this peasant-bred Dilaram, who was always watching for omens. He basked in the reflection of Nur Mahal's splendor, and felt content as long as he knew his mistress to be untroubled.

And it seemed to the old eunuch that Nur Mahal had found peace of mind after the struggle of her early life. Deftly, she watched over the heads of the government and avoided quarrels. She read through a report in the time it took him to master the first words. She had the rare ability to look ahead and escape difficulties that would have set men to wagging their beards and clutching at sword hilts.

More than that, she had an instinct for selecting able men for office. Once appointed she trusted them, but watched them—so that the weaker among them were not tempted to enrich themselves by fraud, knowing that they were watched. Waste she would not tolerate. Even the gold-embroidered covers that came with letters of state and had been thrown aside before then, she ordered made into saddlecloths and elephants' headgear. When she drew up a land grant, the Kadr of the Empire approved it, having learned by experience that it was useless to oppose her.

She made a point of reading over the criminal cases, drawing her pen through so many decrees of punishment that Jahangir christened it the Pen of Mercy. But Ambar noticed that she never pardoned one who intrigued against Jahangir.

The eunuch no longer feared that anything could destroy Jahangir's love for his mistress. As the emperor grew weaker and more intent on his own amusements, his need of the beautiful Persian increased. Without her, he became restless and petulant —declaring that he was no more than half alive. He seemed to take pleasure in making display of his love, until even the sophisticated poets of the court could not conceive of Jahangir existing without Nur Mahal.

"Was ever a woman before," Farrash asked,

"courtesan and wife, nurse and love-player, verse-maker and councilor of state?"

"And commander of thirty thousand horse," Nasiri assented.

"I would give thee all those horsemen for a particle of Nur Mahal's favor. She cares nothing for poems of praise, and now that Jahangir has her, he will listen to nothing else than praise of her."

It had become clear to the poets and courtiers that the road to favor no longer lay through Jahangir's good-nature. They found it necessary to send petitions in to Nur Mahal, and if she granted an audience they must needs stand before a veiled woman who looked through them with disillusioned eyes, a little compassionate and more than a little amused.

Farrash, for one, had not prospered. Jahangir no longer gave away palaces in his cups, and Asaf Khan, the poet's patron, did not initiate such orgies as formerly.

"When Kurram surrenders, there will be a festival," Nasiri suggested.

Farrash shook his head. "Jahangir might pardon the prince," he objected, "but Nur Mahal will never forgive the murder of Khusrau."

"They must pardon Kurram—who else is to be heir of the empire?"

"Allah—or Yahweh and all the gods may know. Nur Mahal could make an heir out of dust and water, but she will not recognize Kurram so long as Jahangir breathes."

The prophecy of the poet proved correct. Kurram, who had carried the civil war from the Dekkan to

Bengal and the north, was finally stripped of followers by the genius of Mahabat Khan. The Rajput princes who had rebelled were slain in battle, and the traitor Abdullah turned dervish and was seen no more. Kurram, hunted from pillar to post, decided to throw himself on his father's mercy. Through Asaf Khan he sent a letter acknowledging his guilt and protesting that he was very ill.

The letter, addressed to Jahangir, was meant for Nur Mahal, and to her Asaf Khan made a plea for leniency to be shown the prince.

"Mihri," he urged, "Kurram long hath been the prop of the empire: who but he can ascend the throne after—when the hour appointed arrives? Do not add the poison of hatred to the blood of this war."

She looked once at her brother and turned away. "The poison was given to Khusrau when he was in his brother's keeping. And the blood was shed when Kurram led an army against his father."

The prince's life was spared, but he was made to surrender his two remaining fortresses, to send his two sons Dara and Aurangzeb to court as hostages, and to retire to an estate in the Dekkan—without permission to approach his father again.

This last condition troubled Asaf Khan, who had hoped for much from the prince, his son-in-law, while he continued to serve Jahangir with imperturbable good-nature. "An exile," he confided in Farrash, "is no better than one who is blind and dumb. Kurram's path would be easier if he were a captive behind Gwalior's gate."

"The wheel of Fate turns," Farrash remarked tentatively, while he reflected that Kurram's defeat had been due to Nur Mahal's quickness of thought, and his exile to her determination. Jahangir no doubt would have allowed his brilliant son to return to court, after much outward show of anger. But the Persian had been careful not to make a martyr of him.

"Ay, but slowly," Asaf responded. "A hand that aided Kurram now would have reward, when the wheel has turned."

It was a casual remark, yet Farrash scented a hidden meaning. "What could bring solace to the prince," he wondered aloud, "now that the gates of mercy are shut against him here, and his war standard has been broken? Alas, he must live his days without sight of Arjamand's two sons."

They were Asaf Khan's grandsons, he knew, and he waited to hear what the wealthy Master of the Household might choose to say.

"Kurram ever enjoyed a well turned verse—and a gift."

Farrash almost smiled. The matter-of-fact Kurram, of all men, had no sympathy for poets. Obviously, then, Asaf wished him to go to the prince's estate. But the gift? "It is my kismet," he declared, "that I have no present worthy of such a prince."

"Perhaps I might find one."

Not until the poet had made ready for his journey into the Dekkan did Asaf Khan entrust to him the gift to be taken. And at the first halting place, when he was secure from observation, Farrash dismissed all the servants from his pavilion and examined it with minute care. He knew Kurram's temper, and he had no intention of carrying a token that might offend the exiled prince. On the other hand, if Asaf Khan had sent something that might compromise either of them with the Mogul, Farrash desired to know it. Asaf Khan, being a loyal servant of the Throne and Nur Mahal's brother, was above punishment, but he himself might be given to the torturers. Then again, if the letter were sufficiently compromising, he might sell it for a good price, or blackmail Asaf Khan.

Fortunately he did not have to break a seal, as the heavy, folded paper was loosely tied with silk cords. He spread out the paper with an exclamation of surprise. There was no writing on it, but within it, wrapped up in silk, he found four different objects.

"He hath sent a message by tokens," the poet murmured.

Tokens were common in a land where not everyone could write, and where women often found it convenient to send messages that had meaning only for a lover's eye. These four objects, however, proved puzzling. A broken, tiny iron ring with a fragment of chain—obviously from the claw of a falcon. Broken fragments of a woman's glass bracelet. A length of twisted camel's-hair cord. And a flaming blossom from the *palas* tree.

This last signified loyalty, the poet reflected. While the cord was the kind used to bind packs upon animals—most probably the sign of a journey. The broken bracelet could mean a woman who had lost her husband—Hindu women had their ornaments taken or broken from their arms upon the death of their lords. Was a Hindu meant? Or merely a widow?

The hawk's chain might be almost anything. But the other three parts of the message would be meaningless unless the significance of the broken chain were known. . . . A broken chain . . . freedom from captivity . . . a falcon released to fly in the air.

"Kurram must know more of such things than I," Farrash assured himself, "if he sees meaning in all this. "Who is loyal, and who is to make a journey? What is the widow?"

It occurred to him after a moment that the whole message depended upon the order of reading the signs. He tried fitting the signs to living persons. The widow offered possibilities. Possibly Nur Mahal—but she was married at present, of course— or Khusrau's widow. The loyal man obviously would be the sender. So, it might be read—Nur Mahal a widow, Asaf Khan loyal, freedom from bondage, a journey.

Farrash perceived in this some vague meaning, but no definite message. He grew tired of cogitation and wrapped up the tokens again.

"Three things are certain," he summed up to himself. "Asaf hath sent a secret message which hath meaning for Kurram alone. And something is about to happen."

He decided that it would do no harm to deliver the tokens; but he had no wish to share Kurram's life in exile, so he announced to the prince, when he arrived at the jungle-enclosed Balaghat, that Asaf had requested his prompt return to court. Without seeming to do so, he watched Kurram's fingers intently as the prince opened the packet and moved the objects about on the carpet before him. Kurram no longer sat in a throne-chair; his pointed beard showed streaks of premature gray, and his cold brown eyes had the stare of a basilisk. Farrash was glad that he did not depend upon the mercy of those eyes.

Kurram arranged the tokens in the following order: the broken bracelet, the palas blossom, the cord, and the broken hawk's chain. This seemed to satisfy him, because he swept them all together and tossed them aside as if valueless.

"Say to thy master, Asaf Khan," he instructed the poet, "that the hawk will not take the air until the quarry be slain."

During his long return journey, Farrash reflected upon this, without satisfying his curiosity. Kurram had understood the tokens, and had given Asaf Khan an answer that might mean anything. This, evidently, was an unusual hawk, since it would not fly until the game had been brought down by others.

He learned nothing from the Master of the Household when he delivered Kurram's reply.

"A year ago," Asaf Khan observed idly, "I sent a brown gerfalcon to the prince, but it seems that the bird was not properly trained to take the air."

"Ah," the poet nodded understanding. "Yet the sun of your generosity illumines all your servants."

Asaf Khan signed to an attendant to give him a purse as reward for his journey. It was heavy in the

hand, but Farrash knew by the sound it gave out
when he grasped it that it held only silver. A nig-
gardly reward, he thought, for bringing a message
from the end of the empire—a message that could
not be read.

Not long after Kurram's surrender the first attempt was made to poison Jahangir. The tasters of
the kitchen noticed nothing amiss in the dishes prepared for him, but a slave girl stole a silver cup of
almond cake, and sickened after she had eaten it.
That day Jahangir had barely touched the dishes set
before his knees, and when physicians examined the
remnants of the feast they found poison in the minced
chicken and almond cake.

Nur Mahal had been awaiting such an attempt,
knowing that with the death of Khusrau an effort
might be made to end the Mogul's life. She swept
even the porters from the lashgar's kitchen and in-
stalled her own people.

But the poison lingered in Jahangir's mind. He
contemplated it in his methodical way, wondering
who would try to destroy his body. Dismissing the
poets from his table, he made a journey to the home
of a Hindu ascetic, who had impressed him by silence and by utter indifference to his own questioning. The last stage of the journey he walked pain-
fully afoot, until he came to a nest of boulders on a
hillside, and the mouth of a cave too small for him
to enter. There he bent his head in salutation to the
emaciated man whose fingers were horned talons.

Jadrup Gosain passed his years in a cave too small to permit him to stand erect.

Stroking his hand, the Mogul sat by him. The hot sun flashed on the emerald in Jahangir's *pagri,* and on the folds of his satin vest. He talked well—had he not listened by the hour to the discussions of the priests?—and seemed content with the silence of the holy man.

"Is it not true," he confided, "that men are governed by reason, while the animals live by instinct, which is from God?"

The ascetic stirred, lifting his head. "O Padishah, does their reason suffice men?"

"Surely it raises them above the animals."

Jadrup Gosain never argued like the impassioned mullahs or the eloquent Jesuits. The vistas of his meditation were too clear. "If that contents them," he responded after a long silence, "it is because they desire nothing more."

But Jahangir, in spite of his indolence and his partiality to other faiths, could never quite banish the doctrines of Islam from his mind, although he spoke always of God, seldom of the prophet of Islam. "Our lives are ordained," he argued with boyish insistence. "We follow an invisible path, and we pass through the grave to what awaits us beyond? Is it not so, O holiest of men?"

"I know it not. . . . We can only seek the Way."

Comforted, Jahangir nodded, and departed from the hermit, cheerfully exclaiming upon the wisdom of this one who had withdrawn from the sins of the world. His contemplative mood lasted for some time, and Nur Mahal heard that he had engaged two antagonists in debate—an orthodox mullah, and a Christian priest from Goa.

When he had listened long enough, Jahangir asked them if they had faith in the Koran and the Bible to preserve them by a miracle. Both, eyeing the other, assented, and he suggested that a pit be dug and wood piled in it and set afire. The two, then, would enter the pit, holding in their arms respectively the Koran and the Bible—so that all could see which would be burned and which emerge unharmed.

Apparently both the champions were willing to undergo the test. Each, however, wished the other to enter the fire first, and in the end Jahangir laughed and freed them from the ordeal. After that he called the Christian Father Fire.

That same day, in the evening, he gave command to have elephants fight on the parade ground. Sitting under his canopy, he watched with delight while the great beasts were led toward each other on opposite sides of a mud wall, until they trumpeted their rage, and the shock of the clashing tusks shook the ground. When the slight wall was battered down by their lunges, one of the beasts forced the other back—slaying the mahout with a sweep of his trunk. The riderless elephant, gashed and shaken, was forced down toward the river. They plunged into the water, and could only be separated by flaming torches in the hands of their keepers. . . .

Satiated after a half dozen bouts between the elephants, Jahangir sought Nur Mahal's pavilion that night, to give her his impressions.

"My mind is refreshed, O my Soul," he explained at the end of his account of the day—the events of which she had already heard from her own people. "But still the holy man was so silent—perhaps he did not say all that lay in his mind. Thinkest thou the grave could separate us?"

"Who has endured the dread of separation," she murmured, "need not fear the Judgment Day."

"What is that?" he asked quickly. "One of thy Persian verses?"

"My own thought, O Shaikhu Baba. What could part us—now?"

"Eh—what could have come between us, in the past?" he demanded jealously. His passion had taken a new aspect, with the increase of his illness. Now he demanded that she be always within summons, so that he could feel she was waiting, to hasten to him. Irritably he complained of the hours she spent in conference with the ministers.

"My enemies would have come like snakes between us," she responded.

"And now?"

She smiled, with the swift curving of cheeks and flash of eyes that always stirred him. "Now we will go hand in hand, Shaikhu Baba, to the Last Day. I feel it is so."

The concept pleased him. Long since, he had learned to give heed to her instinct more than to any words. He himself doubted much if there would be any Judgment, when Solomon would sit before the suspended chains and the souls of the faithful would gather below the Rock. But Nur Mahal, who was so much cleverer than he, prayed with the faith of a child.

Gently he stroked her face, letting his fingers dwell upon the slender throat. "Thou art altogether happy, heart of mine?"

"More than happy, Shaikhu Baba." She nestled close to him, her dark head against his swollen cheek.

Jahangir felt pleasantly reflective. "It is written that when husband and wife join hands, their sins slip from their fingertips. God knows how many have been my sins." He sighed without deep regret, unaware of the sudden tensity in her dark eyes. "Thou knowest how I vowed never again to shoot beasts with a gun—I only caught them in nets thereafter, until the Rebel's disgraceful behavior drove the vow from my mind, and in anger I began to shoot game. In this one moon I brought down seventy and three antelope."

"The hunting restores health to thee," she said frankly, "and thy life is the safeguard of thy people."

"I feel it is so. But when I have entered the grave, what will befall thee, Mihri? Parviz will succeed to the Throne, because he with Mahabat Khan will hold together the army and exact obedience. Then the reins of government will lie in thy hands."

It was the first time that Jahangir had mentioned death, and something cold touched her heart. "Nay, Shaikhu Baba," she cried, "my hands will keep thee from the grave."

"For all of us, Mihri," he said with dignity, pleased with her real distress, "there is an hour and a place appointed. Parviz must be Padishah after me—Shahriyar is young and weak. His brothers would blind him and put him in Gwalior."

At the back of his mind lay regret that Kurram the dominant and ever successful would not be able to succeed to the Throne. Jahangir, so long as actual proof was lacking, could pardon the murder of Khusrau, while to Nur Mahal a brother who had slain a brother was beyond mercy.

"Thou art the only Padishah!"

"Nay, I am God's servant." Jahangir was still full of his conversation with the hermit. "My life is devoted to my people and to thee."

Nur Mahal worried over his new mood when he left to seek a wine cup in the Bath-house. Later that night, when her slaves told her the Padishah's lights were still burning, she wrapped herself in a mantle and went to the pavilion, where she slipped into her place behind the screen without being observed. She wondered if Jahangir felt weaker, or if some new poison had been put into his drink, despite all precautions.

She found him kneeling on a sheet with one of the animal keepers, intent on a pair of frogs which were being trained to catch dummy sparrows. At a touch from a blade of grass, the frogs would leap on their prey, grappling the dummies with their short forelegs and rolling over, while the Mogul chuckled delightedly.

Nur Mahal found her hours too occupied for reflection. She was free, yet she was caught in the surging demands from thousands who pressed about her. On journeys, looking down from the *pitambar* on her elephant, she saw how the villagers drew away into the fields of high grass at her coming, and how the saffron-robed priests of the temples came out to look at her curiously before turning away to their talk. To these people, the empress was still an alien, un-purified, a breaker of the Law.

She had been permitted to approach as far as the courtyard of a temple once, to see the inner darkness between the carved stone pillars, where the young *devadasis* sat—the half-grown girls, impudent and yet forlorn, who served the wooden image of the god Jagganath, and who stared hostilely at the veiled white figure of the stranger.

From such as they she was severed by age-old tra-dition. With their lives, bound to the service of the gods, to the fertility of the fields and the children who were born and died, she had no fellowship. They stood guard between her and the curtained shrines . . . she thought of Prithvi, crying out be-neath the motionless arms of the smiling god Siva. To these children of the temples Prithvi would have seemed unclean, an outcast who had gone to the arms of the barbarian conqueror. And yet Nur Mahal, who had wandered, at their age, over the caravan roads with her father, pitied them.

Of Lardili, who now had a girl-child, she thought gratefully. Her daughter's life lay apart from the court, and Shahriyar was a kindly boy—never ap-pearing in the Mogul's hunts or the council assem-bly.

When Lardili had been absent from the Agra harem for six months, Nur Mahal sent for her, and waited with growing impatience when she still delayed. When she arrived and made the salutation of greeting before her mother, Nur Mahal noticed a change in her. The girl's round cheeks had fallen in, and her eyes moved restlessly.

Deftly, she led the talk to Lardili's home, until she mentioned Shahriyar's health. He was well, it seemed, but Lardili's hands twisted tight in her lap when she said so. In a few moments Nur Mahal had satisfied herself that the young prince had committed the offense of devoting himself to some of the Gilded Ones, the Hindu singing girls.

"Yet," she smiled—Lardili was not long a bride— "he hath taken no other woman to wife, and now thou hast a child to bind him to thee. Say nothing to him about these others, who are no more than slaves."

"If he would not touch me!"

Lardili wept, and all her mother's wit could not draw from her the inner reason of her grief. Nor would the girl remain long at Agra. Nur Mahal decided to summon Shahriyar to her, knowing that she could learn from the young prince what Lardili had concealed. With one excuse after another Shahriyar delayed coming, until more serious matters distracted the Persian.

For one thing, the hot season held Agra in its grip, and Jahangir urged her to begin the summer's march to the northern hills. While she was pacifying him and preparing the lashgar anew, her brother Asaf

Khan arrived from Bengal with tidings of disturbance along that always unsettled border.

"A division of the army is needed," he complained. "But it would avail more to send a leader who could stamp out the sparks of unrest. Send Mahabat Khan, who is chewing the cud of idleness."

"The Sirdar is Parviz's companion."

His plump face expanded in a tolerant smile. "Now that the rebellion is ended, O my sister, is it good to keep the Sirdar idle? Nay, give him a task worthy of him."

For a moment she studied her brother, wondering at his request. Of course Mahabat's presence would pacify Bengal nicely—and the Master of the Household ever loved the easiest way of dealing with trouble—but she suspected he wished to score against his old adversary.

"Why not send Khan Jahan Lodi?" she ventured.

"Good—except that a swordsman, not a councilor is needed."

When she thought the question over, she decided to order Mahabat Khan to go. For the moment he was the hero of the public, with the army, Parviz, and a treasure under his hand. Better to put him to work again, while keeping Asaf with the lashgar. So the order went, and before her preparations to leave Agra had ended she received an answer from Parviz. The prince objected to separation from the great Afghan.

Actually, she knew, the decision had been made by Mahabat Khan, and she could not let the Sirdar dictate to her. Summoning Fedai Khan, whom she could trust under all circumstances, she gave him a direct order to carry to the army.

"The Padishah says, let Mahabat Khan go to take command of the imperial standard in Bengal, or come to give explanation before the Presence."

The officer touched his hand to his forehead impassively, but did not ask for leave to depart.

"What is it?" Nur Mahal asked.

"The Sirdar will ask of me, who desires him to draw his rein to the court, and why?"

Impatience at the routine thought of men, and the interminable need of conciliating them overcame the Persian for a moment. Because she was a woman, they demanded assurance from her. Would Mahabat Khan have questioned an order from Jahangir ten years ago?

"Oh, there is need that he come to account for the elephants taken from the Dekkan princes, and to give an account of the treasure now with the army."

"As the Most Imperial hath said, the words shall go to him." Fedai took his departure, and Nur Mahal turned to the hundred details that awaited her, before Jahangir could begin the summer march. His eyes had been troubling him, and he fretted at delay, while the sandy plain around Agra became a furnace.

They were on the way at last, the imperial parade filling the trunk road to the hills, when Nur Mahal received the Sirdar's answer. He was on his way to the court, sending the elephants ahead, and in the Presence he would make a full accounting. The mes-

sengers added that he had an escort of some five
thousand Rajputs with their families.

Having a long start of the Afghan, the lashgar,
although moving much more slowly, had reached the
high plains through which the river Jhelum cuts its
way, before the elephants appeared on the road, and
word came up that Mahabat Khan was within two
rides of the imperial camp.

And Nur Mahal felt relief from the worries of
the last months. Already Jahangir had revived, in
the cooler air from the purple foothills. The camp
was pitched in groves of plane and willow trees on
the bluff above the river, murmuring over its sand
bars. The long grass by the water's edge swayed
under the wind's touch.

The Mogul had become absorbed in a caged tiger
that had taken a fancy to a goat. Jahangir sat outside
the cage for hours, watching the strange pair, and
making experiments—taking away the favored goat
and putting another in its place. The tiger, he
noticed, sniffed at the substitute and then broke its
back with the stroke of a paw; it also killed and then
ate a sheep put into the cage. But when the first goat
was returned, the tiger played with it contentedly,
and Jahangir marveled. . . . To Nur Mahal, his
good spirits were an omen of health.

She waited for Mahabat Khan's arrival, confident
that once she was face to face with the Sirdar, his ill-
humor would vanish. "But what keeps him from the
lashgar?" she asked Ambar, when three days had
passed. The great camp had been taking its time
crossing the river on a single bridge of boats—the

cavalry and baggage trains were now quartered on the far side.

When the eunuch could not enlighten her, she sent for Fedai Khan, and discovered that the imperial messenger had just returned to the lashgar. He saluted her gravely.

"The Sirdar waits in his tents because the order was given."

"The order?" She looked up at him, puzzled. "The order was, to come to the Presence."

"I carried it myself two days ago to his quarters. It bore the handprint of the Padishah."

So Jahangir had signed a command unknown to her—a thing he rarely did unless in his cups. But who had presented it to him? Fedai Khan acknowledged regretfully that he did not know.

"What is upon thee?" she asked suddenly.

The young officer flushed. It had been his pride to carry the confidential messages of the empress, and he had no other ambition than to serve her, who held his youthful devotion.

"By Allah, I am thinking what will happen when the Sirdar comes. Truly the youth deserved punishment, but what availed it to cast shame upon the Sirdar in this fashion?"

"Shame?" Sudden misgiving swept over her. "What means this?"

"The punishment of Barkhudar, O Most Imperial."

She shook her head. "I know not the name."

For once Fedai Khan seemed to doubt his mistress, and his voice faltered. "Thus it befell: in the last moon the daughter of Mahabat Khan was married to Barkhudar. I know little of that, but some say it was without the consent of the Padishah. Now, in these two days, the command is given to lead out Barkhudar, to strip turban and slippers from him, to hang him up by the heels and beat the soles of his feet until he can no longer walk. Moreover, at spoken command I was sent to take by force the chests of the girl's dowry, given her by Mahabat Khan."

Nur Mahal's face grew bleak, and she struck her hands together. If she had planned to insult the Sirdar, it could not have been done more effectively. The offense—if the marriage had taken place without the formality of the emperor's consent—had been slight, and the Sirdar's son-in-law had been treated as a low-born criminal. Even the girl's trinkets had been taken from her, and by Fedai Khan, her own messenger.

"How—who gave the command?" she cried.

"The brother of the Princess."

"And why was I not told at the time?"

Gravely Fedai Khan bowed before her anger. "The exalted Asaf Khan gave the order in the name of the Padishah. And surely I, the servant of the Most Imperial, have not the right to question an order."

Even Fedai Khan, she thought, believed that she had planned to disgrace the Sirdar's daughter—after first ordering him to remain away from the lashgar. After summoning him from the army, to this. The effect of it was worse than if dirt had been cast on the Sirdar's beard in open audience.

She doubted if Jahangir had known anything of it. Her brother had planned it skillfully, to antagonize Mahabat Khan, who would naturally believe she had done it.

"Go thou to the Sirdar—nay, first bid my brother come to my khanate."

But Asaf Khan was across the river with all his people. Going to the entrance of her quarters she could see the distant camp fires winking like red eyes in the twilight. A belated stream of laborers and loaded camels was moving across the boat bridge. Her Pathan troopers were coming, to take their posts for the night guard.

A stone's throw away the scarlet canopy of the Bath-house glowed as candles were lighted. She heard the tinkle of guitars, and guessed that Jahangir had already seated himself with a troupe of dancing girls whom he had chosen for his dinner companions. . . . She waited, while the river gorge became dark and the stars gleamed over the last of the sunset glow. One of the troopers, unconscious of her presence, caught the melody of the guitars, singing hoarsely to himself:

> *"No vulture am I,*
> *An eagle am I, to strike down my prey!*

> *"No bullock am I,*
> *A tiger am I, to stalk my foe!"*

After the muezzin somewhere over the water had called the last prayer, a galloper came from Fedai

Khan, saying that Asaf held a feast that night, sitting in talk with his guests, and would not visit his sister until the morning. . . . When her maids begged her to sleep, Nur Mahal stretched herself on her silken quilt, listening to the evasive tinkle of the guitars, and the chuckling of the flooded river. She did not sleep until the Bath-house was wrapped in silence, and she knew that Jahangir, dull with wine, had gone to his bed.

It was then that Mahabat Khan came to his king.

They had drawn nearer during the night, he and five thousand Rajputs. They filed out of the tall tiger grass when mist began to cover the river, and the earth turned gray. The Afghan had given his orders, and they knew what to do.

Two thousand of them made a circuit of the Mogul's tents, down to the river's edge and the boat bridge, where astonished guards yielded up their weapons. The Rajputs dismounted, stretched stiffened limbs, and sent a messenger back to report to Mahabat Khan that they held the bridge. They were to allow any of the Mogul's men to cross to the far side, but to permit no one to return. Hidden under the mist, they waited expectantly for tidings from the imperial enclosure.

Thither Mahabat Khan had gone at once with his officers, two score of them riding ahead of the main body. The few servants who waked at the sound of horses approaching took them for the night guard. Through the enclosure gate the Sirdar rode, past yawning sentries, and troopers asleep in the guard

tent. The swirling dust hid him for the few moments
needed to reach Jahangir's sleeping pavilion, where
he flung himself from his saddle. Someone cried
out:

"Mahabat Khan comes!"

With his officers he strode across the empty carpet
of the reception chamber. Mutamad, a secretary who
had the duty of writing Jahangir's memoirs, hastened
out with several eunuchs.

"What means this presumption? Go back, and I
will announce you."

Mahabat Khan only signed to his men to tear
down the screen partition. Swords smashed through
the lacquer work, and the bamboo frame came down
with a crash, as frightened eunuchs tried to waken
Jahangir by rubbing his feet and whispering that he
must rouse himself. But he slumbered heavily, and
only the shattering of the partition woke him, to gaze
with bloodshot eyes into the set face of Mahabat
Khan.

Raising himself on one arm, the Mogul glanced
at the broken screens and the bearded faces of the
Rajputs.

"What a coming is this?" he demanded, blinking.

In spite of the cold determination that had
brought him through the night and past the emperor's guards, Mahabat Khan felt the sting of his
lifelong loyalty to this stout and weary man.

"I have come to the Presence," he said grimly.
"To account for my own deeds."

There was no cowardice in Jahangir, and at the
words he caught up the sheathed sword lying beside

him. Rising unsteadily to his feet, he tried to free the blade.

"O Heaven-born," one of his own officers spoke in Turkish behind him, "this is a time for patience—a true test of a king. I have seen a hundred enemies about this tent, and still they come in at the gate."

With his hand on the scimitar hilt Jahangir stood motionless. "Namak haram!" he cried at his Sirdar. "False to the Salt!"

Mahabat Khan paced the length of the sleeping room, his hands gripping his arms against his chest. He had made no move to touch his own sword, and his gaunt face looked gray in the half light. He had acted on impulse, although he had brooded long on his injuries. When he had heard of his daughter's disgrace and had listened within a few hours to the tale of a spy—that the Mogul remained in the fragment of a camp with no more than a few hundred officers and servants and the harem guards on this side the river—he had made decision to take the sick man captive, and make an end of all intrigue, with the sword.

"I have come myself," he said slowly, "and by Allah it was time. Who is traitor—I or the enemy who accused me in whispers and summoned me hither, ay, and bastinadoed Barkhudar while I waited permission to speak? Now I am here." He turned to the frightened bath servants. "Bring basins and water—wash your master and clothe him."

Ordering his men to remain in the anteroom, he went to the entrance. A glance showed him the crested *pagris* of the Rajputs filling the enclosure—the dark faces glowing with excitement and triumph. Someone told him that the bridge was held, that the Mogul's cavalry guard had been beaten off without serious fighting. The other attendants were waiting helplessly, knowing by now that Jahangir was a prisoner in the hands of his general. An Arab officer had been disarmed, and others were flying across the river.

"Patrol the bank," Mahabat Khan ordered, "send for the rear guard to come in."

"And the bridge, O Sirdar?"

"Let it remain as it is." The Afghan had no wish to take many prisoners. When Jahangir emerged from the tent the nearest Rajputs dismounted respectfully, and Mahabat Khan made the *taslim* of greeting, going himself to hold the stirrup of the charger that awaited the Mogul.

But Jahangir, who had recovered from his utter astonishment, drew back. "This is no horse of mine! Shall I ride out on another's charger?"

A little thing—Jahangir realized that he was in the hands of his general, yet would not be seen in the rôle of a prisoner. Mahabat Khan ordered a horse to be brought from the imperial stable, and asked his master to accompany him about the encampment. All the servants of the sleeping tent had been put under guard, and those at a distance would not know what had taken place between the Mogul and the Afghan. If they saw Jahangir riding quietly before his general, there would be no fighting for the present—and Mahabat Khan wished to avoid armed combat.

For a while there was a tumult, when a faithful mahout rode up on Jahangir's favorite elephant, only to be slain by the Rajputs. Jahangir had a moment for reflection. "I would like to change," he suggested, "to hunting dress, if we are to ride far."

"What need, my Padishah?"

"I wish it. The dress is at hand, in the tent of the princess."

Mahabat Khan gazed at him blankly, and turned to the officers behind them. In the suspense of the attack he had taken no thought for Nur Mahal.

"Go thou," he commanded. "Take the nearest riders and surround the quarters of the princess. Be quick!"

Dust swirled again through the scarlet pavilions, as the horsemen took their places. Trusting no evidence but his own eyes, Mahabat Khan dismounted at the entrance, bidding the eunuchs request their mistress to approach near enough to him to be recognized. He would not mistake her voice for another's. And while he waited, staring into the shadows beyond the half-drawn curtain, it seemed to him more important to have Nur Mahal in his hands than the emperor.

Quivering with anger and offended dignity, the old Ambar stepped from the curtain.

"Thy mistress?" the Afghan snarled.

Ambar looked reproachfully up at the silent Jahangir. Here was an armed enemy demanding the empress in the very face of the lord of India—who did nothing to prevent!

"Black-hearted dog of the hills!" he shouted.

One of the troopers struck him across the face with the flat of a *tulwar* blade, and Ambar collapsed, moaning. Mahabat Khan could not venture beyond the curtain without breaking a law more ancient than the reign of the first Moguls. Instead he sent in some of the Rajput women who had accompanied his camp. They searched all the pavilions within the ring of troopers and came out empty handed. Nur Mahal was not to be found.

"Go down," Mahabat Khan ordered a rider, "to the bridge of boats. Set fire to it. No one is to cross the river—on thy head be it."

A more thorough search of the camp yielded no sign of the woman he sought. Nur Mahal had vanished without a trace.

She had roused at the first tumult, when her maids began to wail. Going to the entrance she had made out, in the haze of dust and mist, the heads of the Rajput troopers above the cloth wall that enclosed her pavilions, as they surrounded the Bathhouse. Then Javahir, a eunuch, appeared with servants and saddled horses.

"Thy lord the Padishah?" she demanded of him.

"Captive to Mahabat Khan, may God curse——"

"Be silent!"

While others besought her to mount a horse and escape with her guards through the confusion, she thought swiftly—realizing that Mahabat Khan would have enough armed force to hold the imperial quarters—that once he had lifted hand against Jahangir he had accepted the lot of an open enemy.

With half her mind she heeded the panic-stricken exclamations of her slaves, telling her that the guards had been overcome and the royal officers were fleeing across the river to the main portion of the lashgar.

She had no intention of flying into the brush on this side the river with her servants, to be hunted down thereafter by the Sirdar's men. And when she heard that Jahangir, unharmed, had appeared before his quarters with Mahabat Khan, she made her decision—calling for a gray wool over-robe, such as worn by peasant women, and a pair of common sandals. While her women covered her delicate muslin garments with the gray cloak, she bade them separate and try to make their way across the river. Ambar was to remain at the pavilion—only Javahir was to accompany her.

"Then will the Most Imperial mount her horse?" cried that personage in a fever of impatience.

"Do peasant women ride such steeds?" She almost laughed at his confusion, and waved the others back as she slipped from the entrance. A subdued wail went up from the harem people when they saw her venturing afoot into the open among enemies. Javahir, throwing off his embroidered khalat, followed in dismal silence.

Half dazed, he accompanied his mistress through the groups of Rajput horsemen. For a moment she halted to watch the fighting around the elephant, then joined a band of slaves hastening toward the bridge. When Javahir would have assisted her down the steep path, cut up by cart wheels and hoofs, she motioned him away impatiently.

"Get back! What hath a palace eunuch to do with a woman of the people such as I? Follow behind."

With growing terror, Javahir saw her thrust aside by bullock drivers, and when he beheld the armed Rajputs on guard at the bridge end it seemed to him that the only way of escape was closed beyond remedy. Here were the minions of the enemy, undoubtedly searching for all who came from the palace.

Nur Mahal walked slowly, as if afraid of the armed men. She even limped, when a cart driven by a Jat farmer came up behind her. The driver had to stop when she would not get out of the way, and it seemed to the half-conscious Javahir that they argued fiercely, until the Jat moved to one side, and Nur Mahal climbed to the seat beside him.

The cart creaked on, while fugitives hurried by it. It passed within arm's reach of a mounted Rajput officer who reined forward to peer into it, drawing back with a grimace as he scented the load of manure.

Then a drawn sword appeared before Javahir's eyes, and a gruff voice smote his ears.

"Here is one of the emperor's half-men who may have jewels in his breeches. Do thou hold him, Ram Dass."

Voiceless, Javahir found himself a prisoner, while the manure cart trundled away over the loose boards covering the line of boats. It had disappeared up the other bank when a messenger spurred down to the bridge and shouted that Mahabat Khan commanded the ropes to be cut. Some of the Rajputs rode out to the middle and hacked through the great hemp ropes that bound the boats together.

With a crackling of wood, the bridge parted, the ends swinging toward the shores under the thrust of the flooded river. Grass was piled on the boats near him, and smoke rolled up. Javahir watched the gray water flowing between himself and his mistress.

In the reception tent of Asaf Khan, the amirs of the lashgar sat talking without enjoyment. They eyed each other restlessly, feeling the prick of suspicion, and the uneasiness that comes of sitting by, when misfortune strikes.

They had all—except one—been surprised by the onset of Mahabat Khan, and all, save one, felt dull shame at their position. Ill as Jahangir might be, he was their lord, and their names would be upon men's lips, as those who had commanded the lashgar when the Mogul was taken captive. So they talked, searching each other's minds, and still feeling nearly certain that treachery had brought about Jahangir's seizure. Only the young officers spoke rashly of drawing the sword now on his behalf. There were too many reasons against doing so, the chief and unanswerable reason being the Sirdar himself.

"Only the blind are truly wise," Asaf Khan murmured, stroking the jewels of his silver armlet. "Ay, before taking a step they feel the ground before them."

"God sends affliction," assented the pious Kwaja

Abu'l Hasan, who wanted to hear what the Master of the Household would suggest.

But Asaf Khan waited for the others to propose plans, his brown eyes mournful as he admitted that nothing could be done until armed forces were raised and gathered into one command, to lead against Mahabat Khan—the accursed of God, the salt betrayer—and the Khwaja knew in his heart that much water would flow by the broken bridge before an army would take the field against the Sirdar and the finest cavalry in India. Nor would delay aid Jahangir in the slightest, since each noble, hearing that the sick Mogul was captive, would hold fast to his fortresses and wait to make his own choice of leaders to follow.

What ended their talk and raised every head in amazement was the appearance of Nur Mahal. She still wore the peasant overcoat, and when she walked between them her slender shoulders came no higher than the turban crest of the tallest, sitting upon the floor.

"I have come from the side of the Padishah," her clear voice greeted them. "At what hour will you cross the river, to free him?"

For a woman to enter a council was unheard of— for a *maharani* of the empire to speak to them face to face was unbelievable. They stared at the transparent veil, feasting their eyes on the shadow of curling lips, and the arch of her splendid brow. Fedai Khan, wet to the waist, muddied and haggard, was the first to spring to his feet. He had tried to swim the river on his horse with a score of followers

after the burning of the bridge, and had left half of
them in the water or slain by Rajput swords on the
far side.

"Mihri!" Asaf Khan exclaimed.

Quickly she turned to him. "O my brother, nobly
hast thou smirched the honor of Mahabat Khan. A
brave part has been thine, to have thy lord made
prisoner! To leave only servants and elephants to
defend him. By thy folly thou hast brought shame
upon our name—and I did not see thy standard, the
gift of thy lord, raised to give battle, that the shame
be at least cleansed with blood."

"By Allah," muttered Mansur, a cavalry officer,
"she hath a tongue like Ayesha's."

"The Padishah," said Asaf Khan impassively,
"hath sent written command by Mir Mansur that we
are not to attack his camp, so long as he——"

"Let me see it."

Nur Mahal ran her eye down the crudely written
sheet and tossed it aside. "Mahabat Khan had this
written. He desires no fighting, of course. Will you
take orders from him? I saw the mahout of Dad-i-
Illahi slain when he tried to lead the great elephant
toward his lord."

"Yet," Mansur protested, to justify himself,
"Jahangir himself gave me his signet ring to show
to these lords."

"A ring." The Persian threw back her head. "I
see no man here who did not have rank and wealth
from Jahangir's hand. Ye have eaten his salt, and ye
talk of a ring! Why have you not led out the horsemen and elephants for battle?"

Stung into speech, several of the officers explained. They had no more than two or three thousand good cavalry in the lashgar—the rest were archers, matchlockmen on foot, who must be ferried over in boats. A difficult task, with the river in flood. They had found only two fords, and Fedai Khan had made trial of one——

"Receive my gratitude, Fedai Khan," she broke in.

—disastrously, the officers explained. Mahabat Khan with his five thousand disciplined Rajputs had the advantage of the high clay bank on the far side, and the best of the armored war elephants. To attack such a position across a river would be to risk defeat.

"And if ye do not attack, what then?"

There was silence in the council, until Asaf Khan stirred restlessly, and before he could speak, Nur Mahal laughed—an amused ripple of sound that ended in mockery.

"Then ye will eat shame, and your children will taste of it after you, while the sweepers spit on your tombs, saying, 'This lord sat on his cushions while his padishah was put into chains.' "

A murmur, half protest and half agreement, answered her, and she pitched her clear voice above it. "But I will not do it. After the rising of the sun tomorrow, I shall ride back across the river on Alam Goa the lead elephant of the battle line. I shall summon those who are faithful to the salt to follow me. Then, of the others who abide here, it will be said, 'They watched their princess go into battle without them.' "

"By the Ninety and Nine holy names," cried Fedai Khan, "that will never be said of me."

"I did not think so. And thou, Amir Mansur?" The veteran Turk nodded gravely. "If the standard is lifted, I shall join it."

The younger officers shouted fierce assent, some striking their sword hilts. But Nur Mahal turned to her brother, and asked gently:

"What of thee?"

The broad face of Asaf Khan looked cheerless. " 'What is written,' " he quoted, " 'will come to pass.' "

Before sunrise Nur Mahal, who had been joined by a few of her maids, made an elaborate toilet. After bathing she was rubbed with sandalwood paste and clad in the white brocade of ceremony. Ropes of pearls were wound over her slender shoulders and throat, and the diadem of diamonds and cloth-of-silver set upon her dark hair. She wore only a half veil, and when she walked from her brother's harem with one maid, hundreds of the Mogul's men could see that it was really Nur Mahal who went to the kneeling Alam Goa, ascending the ladder to the battle howdah.

She said nothing more to the amirs. They were the leaders, and must make the arrangements. Each, she knew, was at the head of his own contingent, and she wondered if Mahabat Khan would have chosen to advance in that fashion. Her brother's horsetail

standard followed the line of elephants, and the
Khwaja's cavalry flanked them. A gunshot down the
bank Fedai Khan led a company of young ahadis
and other detachments filed off, to cross lower down.
She hoped that the elephants would force the passage of the ford, clearing a way for the multitude of
foot soldiers waiting with boats in the trampled
grass, waiting to follow them. . . . She wondered
what Mahabat Khan was doing . . .

Alam Goa paced forward, the howdah rocking
gently as he felt the water beneath him. Heavy black
leather studded with iron covered his sides, and
lacquered wooden shutters protected her. Two bow-
men wearing chain mail crouched by the mahout,
and horsemen splashed beside the great elephant.
At times, because the ford proved treacherous, the
horses had to swim, but Alam Goa plodded ahead,
the other elephants following in pairs.

They climbed to a sand bar and crossed it, sinking
into the gray water again. The clay bluff drew
nearer, a solid mass of horsemen lining its summit.
Nur Mahal wondered why everyone kept silence.
She could smell mud, and the wet leather of the
caparisoning, and she peered down through the front
shutters. In the shadow of the bluff a line of
elephants waited by the edge of the water—the great
Dad-i-Ilahi, who had carried her so often to the
tiger hunt, in the center of the line.

Now she heard men shouting, and the splashing
beside her grew louder. The silvered helmets of
the riders nodded as the horses struggled against the
current. A little more, and they would be out on the

bank. . . . So many men seemed to be trying to shout at once.

Suddenly a shutter clashed at her shoulder. An elephant trumpeted, and Alam Goa flung up his trunk to answer. She felt the great beast lift his shoulders as he set foot on the bank and swerved without apparent reason. Bright flickers passed by the howdah, and it was some time before she realized that the sun was gleaming on speeding arrows.

Why, the battle had been going on, for minutes. A rider who had pushed past Alam Goa dropped his shield, and then slipped from the saddle to the ground. She watched the riderless horse turn and gallop away from the elephants. And down the river —it set her heart to throbbing with sheer excitement for the first time—Fedai Khan's men were cutting their way up the slope—disappearing from sight over the summit of the bank. . . . Alam Goa had stopped. The men in front of the howdah were crying out anxiously, and she heard their bows snapping. But all the rest was a meaningless welter of sound, until a roar of voices ahead made her peer out of the shutters.

"Din—din—din!"

That was Mahabat Khan's war shout, and masses of the Rajputs were charging down the clay slope, sliding and falling but coming with the impetus of a landslide. The wave of horsemen rolled toward the elephants. The Sirdar had launched his first charge while the advance of the Mogul's men were struggling for a footing on the bank. The Rajputs rode like mad. They swept by Alam Goa as if the

giant beast had been a rock, parting the waters of
a flood.

She heard a man groan quietly near her and saw
that one of the archers sprawled against the howdah,
with his eyes closed and his legs twisting strangely.
When he slid off, under the rearing horses, she
screamed.

Again a shutter rattled, and she heard the woman
behind her weeping.

"*Ai—ai*—what shall I do? Will the princess
look?"

The maid was holding out her arm, and from the
flesh a shaft of wood tipped with feathers projected.

"O my sister!" She flung her arm about her, thinking that this girl knew no more of the battle than a
child in the camp, and she herself—she knew little
more. But she must watch. . . .

The Rajputs had turned down the bank. Why
were the standards of Asaf Khan and Khwaja Abu'l
Hasan still waiting on the sand bar? Only a few
of her brother's riders had come up to the elephants.
Opening a shutter, she called down to a familiar
figure—a eunuch who had stuck doggedly to the
black side of Alam Goa.

"Nizam—Nizam! Ride back to the Khan my
brother. Say to him that this is no time for hesitation. Bid him come forward to me."

When the eunuch had gone, Nur Mahal closed
her eyes, feeling suddenly faint at the odor of blood
and stench of trodden mud. The sun's glare beat
down on the surface of the water. How had the sun
risen so high, unnoticed? Turning to the weeping

girl, she made an attempt to get the arrow out, only to hear the maid scream.

"Nay—it must be broken first."

They were fighting again beneath the elephant. The howdah lurched, and Alam Goa's trunk lashed about him, scattering blood. Gleaming swords cut at it fiercely, and a rider rose in his stirrups to shout at her.

"Yield thee, O bahadur!"

So they called her a brave one. Did they know that Light of the Palace was in the shuttered howdah? By now they must know, yet the fighting went on. Flushed faces agape with frenzy—lance tips that dripped blood—the screaming of wounded horses, and a dull clattering of iron. . . . She looked back anxiously toward the sand bar, and saw only a confusion of horses, elephants, and men, drawing away from her. . . . Suddenly Alam Goa wheeled, smashing back into the water, forcing his way back, with the terrible horsemen slashing at his sides. Only the mahout was on his head now, gripping the iron band between the giant ears. Alam Goa had been hurt in many places and was plunging to safety. He sank deeper into the water, and the howdah rolled as he began to swim, with a Rajput clinging to one of the straps, and beating at the shutters with his scimitar. . . . The great beast rolled, and water swept against Nur Mahal's knees.

When she looked out again they were in mid-river, swimming downstream toward a sand bank. In the gray water floated bodies and bits of wood. She pressed her hands to her face, waiting, for hours it seemed, until the elephant climbed wearily out upon the sand bar.

It was after sunset when she reached her quarters again, having heard the result of the attack. The Mogul's men had been beaten back everywhere, except at Fedai Khan's ford. That daring individual had cut his way through to the imperial tents, but receiving no support had been forced to withdraw along the other bank. Asaf Khan had shown only irresolution, and Khwaja Ab'ul had swum the river, back to safety.

Utterly weary, Nur Mahal dismissed all her servants and flung herself down, sobbing. She wept only a little, passionately, and then slept heavily for the first time in two nights.

In the morning when she was dressed, she found no one waiting for word with her. She ate a little fruit and barley cake alone, and sent for her brother.

After long delay Asaf Khan appeared, looking ill at ease, and saluted her. He was oppressed by bad news, and his hands quivered when he assured her that some of the amirs were breaking camp and marching toward their own citadels. The secretary, Mutamad, had arrived after daybreak with a second warning from Jahangir not to continue the fighting, and the advice that fresh contingents of the regular army had joined Mahabat Khan, who was now preparing to move against what remained of the lashgar.

"And thou?" she asked.

He essayed a smile. "God knows, O my sister, my

hand was shaped for a pen, not a sword. We must seek safety at once."

"You mean, flee like scattered antelope, as the others are doing? What good can come of that?"

Restlessly he threw himself back on the cushions. "Soon or late thou must know it, Mihri. Mutamad came with warning to thee. Jahangir hath——" he chewed at a ringed finger—"they say Mahabat Khan hath obtained a firman for thy death, from the Padishah."

"For my death?"

"Ay, Mihri. The anger of the Sirdar hath turned against thee. They heard him say, 'Kill the parasites that have sucked thy manhood, and thou wilt be a king indeed.' Moreover——"

"And Shaikhu Baba signed it?"

Asaf Khan nodded. "Mutamad swears he did so when drunk. The Sirdar hath plied him with wine, the two drinking together——"

"I know." Her eyes flashed ominously as she pieced together the Afghan's reasons. It was his plan, of course, to justify his seizure of the emperor by making Nur Mahal and her brother appear as traitors. Given time, he might persuade Jahangir of much—but the death order so soon! After the battle, then, Mahabat Khan had felt a desperate measure to be necessary. He was, after all, a soldier, uneasy when dealing with such problems. Still, he must have hated her, to desire her execution.

"Now that the decree is signed," her brother echoed her thoughts, "it will appear that we, who risked our lives to free Jahangir, were the traitors, following thee against the emperor and his general. Mahabat Khan is no merciful foe."

First she had had to struggle against Kurram, and now Mahabat Khan. Would Kurram emerge from his exile, when he heard the tidings of the Jhelum?

"Make ready, Mihri," her brother was saying, "for the journey to my fort at Attock. We must not waste time in talk."

Her attention focused suddenly upon her brother, stirred by a note of satisfaction in his voice. Something in this disaster pleased him. She had never underrated Asaf Khan's self-love or his intelligence.

"By thine order the lashgar was moved over the river, leaving the imperial pavilions unguarded," she cried, her memory searching the last few days. "Through Fedai Khan thou hast sought to blacken my face with the guilt——"

The words ended in a laugh, half hysterical. "Now I see with open eyes. It was thy plan to leave the emperor unguarded, in the path of the Sirdar's anger—and I also was to have fallen between the hands of the Sirdar, a traitress by thy scheming. But why—what was the gain to thee?"

For a moment his brown eyes contemplated his sister, half fearfully and half petulantly. In truth Asaf Khan was afraid. Leaning close to her, his heavy lips whispered: "Mihri, blind thou art still. The hakims know, as I know, that Jahangir's life is measured by weeks, not by years. The amirs are shaping their plans against his death, and thou the foremost of us all—thou art nursing a dying body. Bethink thee of the succession, Mihri. Is the Throne worthless? By the seven hells, this moment is the sa'at, in which our fortune truly begins. With me——"

Swift caution checked his words, although she egged him on at once.

"With thee, fleeing to Attock—what then?"

He lay back, and the expression left his tired eyes. "If you will not trust me, I can tell you nothing."

To his surprise she stood up, drawing away from him and brushing back the tangle of dark hair from her forehead. She smiled, without any joy.

"You are my brother, Asaf Khan, and you speak of seeking fortune from the death of the Padishah, my husband. It is enough."

He rose, watching her under intent brows. "Overweary art thou, Mihri. What is in thy mind?"

"Oh, much. May your dreams be pleasant, Asaf Khan, and your road be smooth. After all, are you not my brother? And is not this guilt of yours, that you have fastened upon me—is it not a little my guilt? Can a woman accuse her brother of planning the Padishah's death?"

"By the ninety and nine holy names——"

"I have heard enough, and it is true that I am overwearied." She nodded reflectively. "So I am going alone across the river, to give myself up to Mahabat Khan."

It was characteristic of Light of the Palace that, having determined to surrender to Mahabat Khan, she did so in her own time and manner. Late in the evening, after he had attended a conference of his officers and had seen Jahangir comfortably established in the Bath-house the Sirdar was crossing to his own tent, close by, when he noticed a screened palanquin waiting at the entrance of his tent.

The troopers on post there—hawk-nosed Afghans, suspicious of anything unwonted—were circling about it with torches, arguing fiercely. Half-naked bearers squatted by the carrying poles, and a eunuch of the imperial harem waited with downcast eyes and folded arms.

"What is this?" the Sirdar asked.

The eunuch salaamed and stepped aside. The shutter of the palanquin fell to the ground, and a woman slipped out, rising to her feet without hesitation or haste, and Mahabat Khan uttered a single exclamation of heartfelt amazement.

"Wallahi!"

Nur Mahal, it seemed, had chosen to come to him without concealment, or attempt to make conditions. She simply stood there, the white figure slender as a young poplar, swaying in the torchlight. And the men who a moment before had been waiting for a word from him, stared as if a magician had summoned an houri out of Peristan.

"Is this thy tent, O Sirdar?" her voice broke the silence.

Mahabat Khan nodded, unable to find words.

"Then, if thou wilt not give me greeting, at least bid me enter. I am thy prisoner."

"What madness is this? Knowest not that the order——"

"For my execution hath been signed? That is

known to me, Mahabat Khan. But will you keep me standing before these men?"

When he had escorted her within—the eunuch waiting at the entrance—she glanced curiously at the plain furnishings and seated herself on the low divan against the tent pole where the oil lamp glowed. A faint scent of rose leaves crept into the air, and the Afghan waited grimly for argument or tears.

But Nur Mahal appeared at ease, even a little amused at his long silence. He had a strange fancy that she was reading his thoughts.

"Are we not enemies, O Sirdar?" she smiled. "Have you no hospitality to offer a foe who surrenders? I am thirsty and a little tired."

He half turned to the entrance to call for sherbet and dishes of food when he remembered that he could not, in honor, harm her if he offered her bread and salt. Shaking his head, he fell to pacing the carpet before her. Without doubt she would try, with her woman's wiles, to gain permission to join Jahangir—the last thing he could allow.

"If thou wilt not offer entertainment, may I read the order of execution?"

The Afghan glanced at her and took a rolled paper from the chest by his sleeping quilt. With a steady voice he read the decree:

"In the name of Allah the Compassionate, WE having become aware of the faithlessness of the Persian woman Nur Mahal, who hath intrigued against the Majesty of the Throne, causing coins to be minted in her name and raising her kinsmen to the highest offices, and

making an attempt by poison to sever the thread of OUR
life—WE command that she be given to the sword of
mercy."

"And it bears," he added, "the handprint of thy
lord the Padishah who heard it read, as thou hast
heard it now."

Just for an instant she caught her breath, the blood
draining from her face behind the veil. But this the
Afghan did not see or hear.

"Who carried the tale of the poison to thee?" she
asked quietly, wondering inwardly how much opium
Jahangir had taken before signing the order.

"Farrash, one of the court parasites, told it when
drunk, in Parviz's tents this last moon."

He checked his stride before her, waiting to hear
her protest.

"What matter who carried the lie," she mused, "if
thou believest? Tell me, O son of Ghiyar Beg, is thy
mind firm? Am I to die?"

It was his turn to think of arguments, while his
lips tightened, and his veined hand clasped and un-
clasped the hilt of the scimitar at his hip. Then he
nodded.

Leaning back against the tent pole she looked up
at him, whispering:

"O fool! Brave, swaggering fool! Then my tongue
is free of restraint. Thou hast been led by the nose,
like a wandering camel. The one who is plotting
against thee sent Farrash, and lashed thee on with
the bastinado—of Barkhudar, thy daughter's hus-

band—staining thine honor. Now thou art raging like a speared boar, at his will."

The Sirdar's keen eyes flashed under shaggy brows. "If this be true, tell me his name!"

"Nay, seek it thyself." She shook her head gently —how could she betray her brother to this man who would never forgive an insult? "Art ruler of India, my lord Sirdar? Canst not seek a little truth?"

"I? God knows I seek no throne."

"Who puts foot in the stirrup must mount to the saddle, as I have learned—" her laugh was like the echo of a golden bell—"as I have learned."

"I serve the Padishah, no one else. And that is true." He flung out a tense hand. "By Allah, and by the Resurrection when deeds shall be weighed against naked souls, I swear it."

"Listen," she whispered.

He ceased his pacing, and became aware of the tinkle of a guitar. It was faint, muffled by the hangings of tents, but after a moment a girl's voice shrilled.

"Listen now," Nur Mahal whispered, and her dark eyes sought his through the veil. The snatch of song came, without sweetness or melody, from the Bath-house.

*"My heart is like a jasmine, spotted with wine.
Lo, when my petals have fallen, I am thine."*

Mahabat Khan remained grimly silent, fingering his beard. At Jahangir's request the singing girls had been kept in the imperial pavilions.

"My heart is like a jasmine—ai—ai—ai!"

"I hear," he said curtly.

Slowly Nur Mahal's hand rose to her veil. She drew off the flimsy silk and let it fall, turning her face up to his. He looked into the dark eyes ringed with shadows of weariness. Still, the slight lips had the trace of a smile, and the white beauty of the woman seemed untouched.

"Now my veil hath fallen—" her eyes held his— "and like thine, my honor is lost. For years I have served my husband—faithfully, faithfully. The sword of mercy will be merciful to me."

A shiver touched her shoulders, and her eyes closed. "Do not give me to the dealers of punishment. Let it be in a quiet, hidden place, by thine own sword."

Mahabat Khan caught his hand from the scimitar hilt, as if it had burned him.

"Doth my face trouble thee?" She sighed and smiled. "It hath caused me trouble enough. See, I veil it again—thus may thy stroke be swift and sure."

She drew a fold of the light mantle from her left shoulder, her bare arm gleaming above her dark head. The muscles twitched in his face, and his eyes glowed like embers.

"Am I a dog?" he whispered, tearing the death decree in his fingers. "Go to thy husband, woman."

Deep within her something that had been the girl Mihri, that had cherished the faceless doll and had somehow survived all these years, was saying softly, "If only *he* had been my prince." But Nur Mahal's lips said nothing as she adjusted her veil and rose.

VII

AHANGIR had been an interested spectator of his own downfall. During the battle of the Jhelum he had taken a seat overlooking the river, and had felt more thrilled by this earnest fighting than by any combat of elephants. When Fedai Khan had launched a charge that penetrated almost to his tent, he had not moved, although arrows fell about him.

Thereafter he remembered little, for the excitement had weakened him, and his asthma made breathing a torment unless he eased it with wine. Some talk he had with Mahabat Khan, some documents he signed—were they not presented by Mutamad and Rai Gowardhan, the steward of Nur Mahal?—and for a while he listened to the singing of the *lulis,* until he could sleep, fitfully, dreaming that strange people came to his side to look down at the Mogul. When his throat stifled him and his chest heaved weakly he cried for Nur Mahal, and they assured him that the sultana had gone a little from the camp.

Something in his mind kept warning him that he no longer had power to give orders, that he was a prisoner dependent on the will of the Sirdar. At times he questioned Mutamad and Rai Gowardhan, who answered vaguely and wrote politely at his dictation. The pain in his body confused his thoughts and left him helpless. Until the afternoon when he woke to find Nur Mahal sitting at his side.

"Mihri!"

Anxiously he peered into her face—a gray mist obscured his sight at a little distance—and felt relieved that she had not been changed by the chaos of the last days. Quietly she dried the perspiration from his eyes with a cotton cloth.

"What became of thee, Mihri? Wert thou as some said, across the river?"

"For a little while, Shaikhu Baba." She smiled, and he settled back on his cushions. "But now my place is here, at thy side."

Curiously, with relief came a weak irritation. He demanded to know what Mahabat Khan meant to do, and what action she had taken after the attack upon him—Mutamad, who had shifted his allegiance with the wind of fortune, had managed to confuse Jahangir's memory of the seizure by Mahabat Khan with the attack at the river. Nur Mahal was quite well aware that hostile ears listened to the Mogul's words, and that, stripped of authority, she could no longer trust even her own steward.

"Hush thee, my heart," she said softly. "Mahabat Khan serves thee faithfully and will permit no harm to come. Instead, we go now to Kabul with him. Only for the present I have resigned to him the seal and authority of the Diwan."

Jahangir tried to think of Nur Mahal without authority to control affairs, and could not. "But what wilt thou do, Mihri?"

"I will be thy nurse, no more."

This contented him. After a moment he remarked that he had wished for a long time to visit Kabul, where many holy men were buried, and excellent antelope hunting could be had.

Outwardly, as the lashgar assembled and resumed its march under the orders of the Sirdar, Nur Mahal occupied herself with her husband's health. Her interest lay with the Sirdar's in keeping Jahangir alive, and no one interfered with her ministration. She realized almost from the first moment that the Mogul knew nothing of the death decree, and very little of the actual state of affairs. For years he had been accustomed to obey her, unquestioning, and now he submitted to the dictatorship of Mahabat Khan without perceiving the difference—that she had governed him to his own advantage, while the Afghan was using him as a puppet until he could raise another to the throne. That other, she knew, must be the drunken Parviz—Kurram being much too ambitious to endure the Sirdar's control, and Shahriyar, the youngest prince, being the husband of her daughter.

While she nursed Jahangir, she snatched at mo-

ments when they were alone to instil into the wavering mind that he was actually a captive, to be released presently in a way that she had thought out,
and that he must play his part by keeping on the best
of terms with Mahabat Khan—even to confiding in
the Sirdar her own unhappiness and anger at her
plight. It was a delicate task, to stir Jahangir just
enough to play the part of a trusting captive. She
took pains to think out futile plans for escape, knowing that Mahabat Khan would realize their futility
and discount them, while he was reassured by Jahangir's babbling.

Meanwhile she studied the Sirdar's moves with
keen interest—the people of her harem were skilled
in bringing tidings to her unperceived. The Sirdar
acted boldly enough. With Rai Gowardhan's aid, he
began confiscation of her nearest possessions, while
sending troops to seize the treasure at Lahore; he
had laid siege to Attock, wherein Asaf Khan had
taken shelter, and when the lashgar wound through
the bare hills toward the walls of that city, she heard
that Asaf Khan had been forced to surrender. With
the other hostages, Kurram's sons, he had become
captive to his old enemy the Sirdar.

Mahabat Khan garrisoned Attock, appointed a
governor over the northern district, sent envoys to
conciliate the Rajput princes, and resumed the
march toward Kabul. There in the hills beyond the
gut of the Khyber Pass, he would be immune against
attack from India.

When in midsummer they arrived at the gray wall
of the mountain city, he arranged for Jahangir to

ride in state through the gate, while servants seated
behind the imperial howdah threw out handfuls of
silver and gold to the crowds. Apparently the victorious general was no more than the boon companion of a contented Mogul.

And well content Jahangir seemed, beyond doubt.
The sight of overhanging snow peaks and wide
clover meadows about a clear blue lake delighted
him, and he demanded that melons be sent to him at
once, while he quoted a favorite verse of his great-
grandfather who had come out of Samarkand to
conquer Kabul.

*"Drink in Kabul castle, and send the cup ceaselessly
    round.*
*For Kabul is mountain and sea, city and desert, in
    one."*

Escorted by the Rajputs, he set out to hunt in the
lofty pastures where the horses could graze as they
marched, and the mountain sheep were found with
the antelope herds.

Seemingly Nur Mahal did nothing to free herself. Actually she was working without respite, gaining touch through her eunuchs with the officers of
the Sirdar's army who might prove loyal to Jahangir. Some of the regular cavalry were friendly, but
saw no opportunity to strike a blow at the powerful
Rajput contingents, in a city peopled with the
Sirdar's Afghans. Nur Mahal bade them wait, in
readiness. Meanwhile she sent messages to men on

the Kabul road, to Fedai Khan and the governors of
the imperial cities, who had remained passive with
their garrisons, awaiting events. In particular she
ordered her eunuch Hushiyar Khan to gather as
many horsemen as he could in Lahore and march
toward Kabul.

She saw nothing of Asaf Khan, nor did she speak
again with the Sirdar, who feared her more than an
army in the field, yet would do her no personal
harm. When her people sought for a hint of what
she planned, she bade them wait and watch. Knowing nothing at all, they still had the impression that
she was shaping events as she wished, when in
reality she had no definite plan.

It was an unexpected riot that shook Mahabat
Khan's confidence and gave her an inkling of the
course to follow. The overbearing Rajputs quarreled
with the Afghans of Kabul about pastures, and the
quarrel ended in a hand-to-hand fight, with eight
hundred Rajputs slain. Mahabat Khan managed to
restore quiet, but he realized the difficulty of a
usurper who must conciliate the different elements
of the army, and he discovered that in Kabul he was
out of touch with events in the great cities.

With the beginning of autumn he set out for
Lahore with his imperial captive and the lashgar,
taking pains to keep the regular cavalry separated
from the Rajputs. And during the march down to
the Khyber gorge he realized that Nur Mahal had
won over a good part of the officers. He found it
increasingly difficult to guard Jahangir, to watch his

various hostages, and to control his allies in the north of India.

"By Allah," he said once to Khwaja Abu'l Hasan, "I have not slept through a night for three moons."

The uncertainty of it plagued him more than any peril. He punished offenders harshly, putting men to death without cause. Only of Jahangir's good-natured compliance did he feel certain—although he suspected that Nur Mahal would make a move to free the emperor when they reached Lahore. Then a courier brought him news of the detachment of two thousand horsemen coming to meet the lashgar, led by the sultana's eunuch Hushiyar. The detachment had halted at Rohtas, a walled town beyond the next river, two marches distant.

Mahabat Khan was rather pleased, it seems, at the prospect of a visible foe, and certainly Hushiyar's two thousand did not appear formidable. It occurred to him to lead out a stronger force of his Rajputs, scatter the new arrivals, and then await the lashgar at Rohtas. While he meditated, a message from Jahangir suggested that to avoid a quarrel between the forces of the lashgar, the Sirdar might absent himself from the next review.

Khwaja Abu'l Hasan appeared at his tent, to urge that Nur Mahal's officers be kept separate from the others during the customary assembly of the troops the next day. To this Mahabat Khan agreed—and departed that night with two regiments of the hard-riding Rajputs toward Rohtas.

He made the distance in a night and a day, only

to find that Hushiyar's force had not reached the
town, which he proceeded to occupy. The tired
horses and riders were resting the next day, when a
Pathan crossed the river and sought the Sirdar.

"The Padishah hath escaped thee," he reported.
"He is in the midst of the sultana's horsemen."

It had been done without a blow struck, and
Mahabat Khan, listening, perceived Nur Mahal's
hand in the manner of it. The usual morning parade
had drawn up at the entrance of Jahangir's tents. By
the Sirdar's previous order, the Rajputs had formed
on one side the roadway, with Nur Mahal's followers on the other, while the elephant bearing the
emperor and his consort paced slowly between the
lines of horsemen, taking their salute.

Midway down the avenue, a regiment of ahadis
had reined forward at a whispered command from
the Sirdar's ranks, and had surrounded the elephant.
The shout of "Padishah salamet!" had rolled down
the lines, and Nur Mahal's regiments had joined the
ahadis. Seeing the emperor once more in command
of loyal troops, the majority of the regular cavalry
had gone over to him, while the Rajputs—outnumbered now—had drawn off with their baggage.

Mahabat Khan had been cleverly tricked, but he
had realized that his power could not last, and he
delayed not an hour in setting out toward the south
with the men who remained faithful to him. He attempted to rally a new army, only to learn that his
treasure convoy had been captured and reinforce-
ments were hurrying toward the sultana. After
making a detour toward Persia, and discovering that

Nur Mahal had launched a division in pursuit of
him, he abandoned his hostages and with his two
regiments headed toward Prince Kurram.

His reign of a hundred days had ended, and now
the hunted war lord joined the exiled prince, who
welcomed him with unfeigned delight. They had
both, by force of circumstances, become enemies of
Nur Mahal. And they were the most formidable
pair in India.

It was then the autumn of 1626. The rains had
ceased when Jahangir made his triumphal entry into
Agra and appeared again before his subjects at the
jharoka window, where two stone statues of Rajput
heroes now stood, mounted on massive elephants—a
monument to the conquest of other years.

Upon Nur Mahal fell the labor of reorganizing
the shattered government. To Asaf Khan, thoroughly
cowed by the hazard of the last months, she entrusted
the treasury. Here his consummate ability would
serve her well, while he would have less opportunity
to intrigue. The command of the army she gave to
the one old servant of the Throne who might be
trusted—to Khan Jahan Lodi, who had taken no
part in the rising against her.

With all available forces Khan Jahan marched
south into the Dekkan, to stamp out incipient revolt
there and to watch the movements of the exiles,
Kurram and Mahabat Khan.

This done, Nur Mahal could turn her attention to
the succession. She could not evade the fact that
Jahangir would die before many months. The great

amirs and the subject princes were all intent on the selection of an heir. To maintain their allegiance to Jahangir, she was forced to give her support to one of the princes, in spite of her instinctive reluctance to do so.

Before she could act, the decision was taken from her. Prince Parviz, who had been racked by debauchery long enough, died suddenly in his camp. Wine, they said, had brought him to the grave; but the men who came to Agra's citadel and talked low-voiced to Nur Mahal, assured her that Parviz had met his end as Khusrau had, by poison.

"By whose hand?" she demanded.

They could not tell her. The poison must have been given a little at a time—perhaps overdoses of opium—and in Parviz's condition it had not been noticed. Truly, wine had proved the Moguls' bane, taking to the mercy of God first the two sons of Akbar, and now Parviz. Kurram alone had escaped its influence.

Nur Mahal's clear mind singled out Kurram. The exiled prince had been at the border when Parviz died, but Kurram had known of Jahangir's captivity —he must have seen Parviz then as the logical choice of a successor, his own most dangerous opponent. And, slowly, Parviz had died.

"Again," she told herself, "Kurram hath slain a brother."

Parviz she had barely seen—knowing him only as a good-natured, sodden man interested in nothing but hunting and the greater sport of war. Yet his death widened the gulf between her and Kurram.

The moody prince seemed to her to bear the brand
of Cain, remorseless and unforgiving. And she herself had driven Mahabat Khan to his side.

There remained only one thing to do. Shahriyar,
the youngest son and husband to Lardili, must be put
forward as Jahangir's heir, and shown to the court
as the next occupant of the Throne. Nur Mahal
shrank from the necessity—weighed all alternatives,
and finally summoned Lardili to her reluctantly.
Long since she had vowed, in her prayers, that whatever her own fate might be she would never set her
daughter's feet within the imperial harem. Lardili
at least would be spared the wakefulness, the matching guile against guile, and the shadow of death.

"Yet, heart of mine," she said to the girl, "there is
no other path to follow now."

And Lardili wept, her hands clenched against her
lips.

To Nur Mahal, intent on the struggle that absorbed all her energy, Lardili's grief seemed cause-
less and weak. She hardened herself against her own
sympathy.

"Would you have Shahriyar taste what befell
Khusrau and Parviz?" she asked harshly. "Verily,
he must make his place secure, with thy help and
mine."

"If he could!"

Strangely, Nur Mahal had grown intolerant of
indecision in others: she had combated it so often in
Jahangir. No doubt Shahriyar was weak-willed,
indolent, and Lardili little better; but he had few
enemies, and she knew that she could administer the

government for him—place capable men at his side, and guide him through the pitfalls of intrigue.

"He must, Lardili. Hast thou forgotten what my lord Jahangir said when Shahriyar's eyes pained him? That it would do little good to doctor him, since his brothers would blind him before long. Wilt thou have a blind man at thy side through life?"

Lardili only wept the more, until Nur Mahal took her in her arms and held her tight. The dark head of the woman pressed against the girl's tousled brown locks, and they whispered together, for a moment at peace.

"Let thy husband come to me, O life of my life."

"He is not well. O, Mother——"

But within a week Nur Mahal saw to it that Shahriyar visited her in the harem. Already she had arranged to have him elevated to higher rank, and she reflected that he had attracted some notice when he had been placed in nominal command of the army mustered for the Kandahar campaign. The talk of his illness she set down to the Mogul weakness for wine, and to Lardili's qualms about concubines. But when he stood before her, a short, fair man of twenty, wearing a rather large turban, she looked at him attentively.

His skin had grown an unsightly red, and he appeared to have shaved his mustache and eyebrows. Briefly she talked to him, advising him to join Khan Jahan Lodi and take command of the southern army. He seemed, however, to have lost his initiative. When she dismissed him she summoned Rualla, the silent Arab physician of the Mogul.

"What manner of illness hath Prince Shahriyar?"
she asked directly. "It hath fouled his face and
dimmed his eyes."

The Arab nodded understanding. "I have seen, O
Most Imperial. It is what we call Dau salab—loss of
hair—and verily, it is not to be healed swiftly."

"But what is it?"

Hesitating, Rualla fingered his beard, and then
answered plainly—it was best to answer Nur Mahal
so, in these last days. "If the sultana permits, the
disease is a form of leprosy, eating away the hair
and sapping manhood. It weakens the body, and a
cure is seldom heard of. Perhaps, by the mercy of
Allah the Compassionate——"

"How comes it?"

"From the touch of one who hath it," he answered
simply.

A dull pain touched her heart—that Lardili's husband should have fallen to this. She thought of the
Hindu women who had been his intimates and knew
the full of her daughter's sorrow. Like to a leper,
and not to be touched! There was the child, of
course, to fill Lardili's arms, and—and surely she
need not nurse such a sickness.

But Shahriyar could never take his place as heir
of the Mogul until he regained his strength. Men
who would accept the rule of a good-hearted
weakling so long as he looked the part of a ruler
would never give fealty to a blotched and hairless
thing, untouchable. Verily, there was no need of
Kurram's poison here.

"See thou to his cure," she ordered the Arab. "On

thy head be it, and forget not that every month is
precious. Say to him that he must keep himself from
the court and from public sight. Go to Lahore—
away from his family."

He salaamed, understanding perfectly. "To hear
is to obey. And who will attend the Heaven-born,
our lord?"

Nur Mahal looked into his somber eyes. "Is not
that my duty? See thou to thine."

When he had departed, she dismissed her maids
and went to sit in the fretwork balcony overlooking
the river, where cool air stirred the bright tulips she
had placed in boxes by the stone lattice. Here Jahangir had come to wake her from the first sleep after
her marriage . . . the sunrise had cast the shadow
of the fretwork across their faces . . . sixteen years
ago.

It seemed to her that men had come into all her
years, to snatch at her, to struggle for her—once she
had not minded that—and to contend with her. Yet
she had never opposed Kurram until his brother's
murder; she had befriended Asaf Khan—was his
rise in rank not due to her influence?—until he had
betrayed Jahangir. And she had tried, until the last,
to keep the loyalty of Mahabat Khan. Yet each in
his way had struck at her. . . . Even as she sat in
thought, cliques of the great amirs were working to
undermine her authority.

She knew they could not quarrel with her manage-
ment of the empire's affairs. The multitudes of
common people had been content, caring nothing
whether Sultana or Mogul actually ruled, so long

as their fields were not trampled, or their villages confiscated. By now the zealot mullahs of the mosques had ceased to preach against the curse of a woman's rule. The coins bearing her head no longer caused talk. Only the ambitious nobles of the ruling class made cause against Nur Mahal—the ambition of Nur Mahal. Ambition? . . . If she could have peace, and an end of the pain that came when she thought of Lardili. Who had to live with a leper.

Jahangir had said that kingship knows no kinship. But he had never held a girl child against his heart —although it delighted him to play with children. What had that Hindu dancer said, under the statue of Siva? "May the child of your body have no sons, because of the sickness that is worse than the plague . . . may your hands be empty."

Truly a woman knew the pain that could ravage a woman's heart. In earlier years Nur Mahal had found satisfaction in the luxury of the Mogul court; the first taste of power had excited her, and the contests of wits with her adversaries had amused her. Now that had all left her, as water runs from a broken jar, leaving nothing behind it . . . Nothing except the determination to save Lardili from harm. Why, not many years ago Lardili had played with dolls.

Pressing her head against the carved stone lattice, Nur Mahal struggled with the grief that welled up, seizing upon her in spite of her will. She did not weep, but she felt that her body, except for this overmastering sorrow, had become stone, like the fretwork that shut her in. There was nothing within her except this passion of grieving—everything else had gone . . . the last of the girl that had been Mihri, died.

When her women appeared to announce that Asaf Khan waited in the Queen's hall to talk with her, she let them bathe her face with rose water and make up her hair, even requesting that they put on one of the smaller diadems.

Her brother complimented her, and discussed some matter of the revenues coming in from her southern *jagirs,* and the latest shipment of English cloth, which she had taken under her personal safeguard. She answered absently, wondering at the real reason for his visit. He did not see fit to inform her that he had just sent Farrash on a mission to Prince Kurram, to carry the tidings of Shahriyar's illness, and had come to discover from her if he could whether the sick prince had actually been warned to remain in Lahore.

"Soon, Mihri," he suggested, "our lord the Padishah will draw his reins toward the paradise of Kashmir, now that the heat increases here. This time, if it suits thy pleasure, I shall put the foot of determination in the stirrup of duty and mount to the saddle of discomfort, to make the journey with you."

That summer in Kashmir passed with the swiftness of a day in the heights. Purple iris fields faded to green; the wind turned chill, and streaks of snow hid the rock peaks. The water of the Dhal Lake became dark, as the sky obscured overhead.

Jahangir had been content to lie in his open palki,

in the marble kiosk built out over the water, watching the waterfowl and examining those caught in the nets of his hunters. The flesh of his face had fallen in, and he could no longer take opium. Nor did he try to dictate his memoirs; lying instead voiceless by the hour, rousing himself only when Nur Mahal appeared at his side.

"Verily," the physicians said, "he would have gone before Parviz to the tomb had she not kept the flame of life in him."

They noticed how the sick man's head turned to follow her, when she left him—to sit with the ministers of state and hear the reports that had been brought up through the passes by couriers. To keep the threads of affairs in hand in the Kashmir gardens was a greater task than at Agra, but she managed to do it between visits to Jahangir, and the only change they noticed in her was a growing impatience with delay. She had abandoned the pretense of consulting Jahangir, although his name was signed to documents by the writers.

Jahangir lingered until after the first cold, when the physicians urged him to begin the return journey. When the lashgar took the road again, it made slow progress, since he had to be carried in a horse litter at a foot pace. The great camp crawled over the rocks of the Pir Panjal Pass and turned downward, escaping from the winds of the heights.

It descended, past the drooping deodars, into a sun-warmed valley where the oak groves cast a welcome shade. Here, the milder air strengthened Jahangir, and the physicians, who had feared that

he might not endure the cold of the pass, promised
Nur Mahal that he would soon be able to sit in the
jharoka at Agra.

They made a halt in the valley, and Jahangir
planned a hunt. He could not sit a saddle, and his
shikaris sent beaters out to the hillside, driving in
the game to a bare slope beneath which Jahangir sat,
with his matchlock resting on a stone wall. As the
deer came into sight, he fired at them with all his old
quickness of eye. Until the moment when he heard a
scream and glanced up, to see a servant fall from the
cliffs at his side and lie like a bundle of clothing
among the boulders.

Those who were beside the Mogul saw his arms
tremble, and he demanded to be taken back to his
pavilion, although the game was still crossing the
slope. Lying on his cot under the scarlet canopy, he
breathed with difficulty, muttering to himself—his
nerves, raw from lack of opium, obviously shaken.

"Allah the Mighty—Allah the Mighty. Life is
taken for life, and blood for blood. . . . Give me
wine."

He demanded that the camp be broken up, and
Nur Mahal put him in his litter, hastening ahead of
the lashgar's camels for two days. At the rest house
of Bhimbar, where the high grass of the plains meets
the thinning oak groves, she pointed to the haze
ahead of them.

"See, Shaikhu Baba, the way is open now."

"Ay, open," he nodded.

But he had not strength to go on. That afternoon
the head of the lashgar appeared, and the tents rose

again round his own pavilion. The elephants filed in
with their burdens, and the cavalcades of the nobles,
all keeping at a distance, to avoid raising the dust
near the sick man. After the sunset prayer the Sky
Lamp glowed, under a clear sky. And Nur Mahal
watched by his side.

Gray was the lined face, the eyes closed, the lax
mouth struggling for breath. For two days he had
taken no food, and now he could not sleep. Once he
turned his head toward her, moving his hand on the
silk cloth.

"Mihri, I sought thy happiness . . . justice, for
thee." He seemed to ponder this, and spoke a few
words in a clear voice. "Has it pleased thee?"

"Thou hast been my life," she answered simply.

For an instant she wondered, hearing the word
justice. Had this man, who was now dying, made her
an empress to requite the injury he had first inflicted
upon her? Struggling against the pain that racked
him, while his sunken eyes held fast to hers, Jahangir
seemed at last a man with all the courage of his
ancestors. And for that instant she felt that she had
been a stranger—a moody girl into whose hands he
had put one plaything after another, to watch her
pleasure as he had watched the antics of his animals
and birds within the cages.

Then the illusion vanished. It was suffering that
invested Jahangir with a last elusive nobility. His
gray lips formed a word which she guessed rather
than heard. "Wine."

Filling a crystal cup, she held it to his mouth carefully. Unable to lift his head, he choked, and the

wine ran down upon the coverlet. She was conscious of a stir behind her, where servants and physicians had gathered beyond the light of the bed lamp. Sibilant whispering came from the entrance, from the eunuchs who had gathered to watch the Mogul's last hours, to tell the tale of it thereafter. The shapes of veiled women came and went. Stroking his hand, she repeated softly, *"'Of nights the souls of men from out their cages flee.'"*

Turbaned mullahs, kneeling outside the pavilion, prayed in low voices, and the talk of the lashgar was hushed while men waited for the expected word. . . . Nur Mahal sat at her husband's side through the death agony, and when early in the morning a physician stood up after feeling the throat and wrist, she looked up silently.

"Tamam shud," he said gravely. "It is finished."

"May the mercy of Allah," she whispered, "be upon him."

Still she sat on the cushions, erect as always, while they closed the dead man's eyes. Eunuchs edged away from the entrance and hastened to the outer tents, while the wailing of the slave women began. *Tamam shud,* the whisper passed through the reception pavilion where the nobles of the lashgar waited. What would happen now? One by one with dignified haste they departed, to talk of the future with their intimates.

"Tamam shud," the Pathan guards whispered to the grooms of the lesser amirs who squatted by the khanate entrance, and they hurried off to warn their masters. "It is finished!"

A physician made his way to the lighted tents of
Asaf Khan, with the tidings. And the Master of the
Household rose from his place to seek his horse lines
where a courier waited leaning against a saddle and
chewing betel. Asaf Khan drew the signet ring from
his finger. "Mount and go," he cried. "Spare nothing in thy going. Jahangir is dead."

As the man salaamed and gathered up the reins,
Asaf Khan said, "Say to Prince Kurram that the
widow shall be a widow indeed. I—his servant—
shall spread the carpet of loyalty in the path of his
coming."

Lashing the horse, the courier galloped from the
tents, seeking the road that would lead him for
twenty days down the length of India to the exiled
prince. Asaf Khan departed to give other orders.

At sunrise four veiled figures approached Jahangir's body. Nur Mahal, beholding these washers of
the dead, left the pavilion and sought her quarters
where Ambar waited at the head of her people. It
was finished, and the current of life that had borne
her through the last sixteen years had changed. She
had become a widow in very truth—a woman without protection, yet still the Most Imperial who had
governed the empire. Her first command was that
her women should not wail. Her second was to send
for Asaf Khan.

The morning passed, and her brother did not
come. Instead a troop of ahadis appeared, and she
heard hot words exchanged between them and her
own guards. Ambar came in to explain that the

anadis had been ordered to relieve her Pathans, who showed no disposition to give up their post. Swords were being drawn.

Veiled, Nur Mahal went to the entrance, crying out to the men to sheath their weapons. "What is this?" she asked wearily.

"These others are not thy servants, O Most Imperial," a Pathan vouchsafed. "Shall we go away from thee like whipped dogs, at another's command?"

The royal troopers, who outnumbered her followers, had surrounded the cloth barrier.

"Who gave ye command to come in this fashion, within sight of the death tent of your lord?" she cried at them.

"At the bidding of his honor Asaf Khan we are here, O Most Imperial," one responded without looking up at her. "Verily it is his wish to safeguard thee in this hour."

"There is no need. You have leave to go, at once."

Still the officer stood his ground, fingering his waist cloth restlessly. "The order was given," he maintained, "and we may not depart."

An ominous grating of steel against leather answered him, for the Pathans had heard a command of their mistress denied, and they were more than ready to sell their lives in protest. They were crowding together and snarling like wolves, when she sent Ambar out to them, ordering them to seek their tents, leaving the ahadis on guard in their place.

"It is the wish of the lord, my brother," she called to them. "And now I give ye command to go."

When the last of her guards had withdrawn, and the ahadis had taken their posts about her camp, she retired to her couch, only to be sought by a eunuch who had been turned back when he tried to leave her gate. "The armed men say," he assured her, "that no one may go forth or come in without an order from the Master of the Household."

"Am I a captive, so soon?" Her dark eyes blazed, and she struck her hands together. Summoning Ambar, she wrote swiftly a message to Lardili and Shahriyar at Lahore, advising the prince to gather as many supporters as he could, to seize the treasure at that city—to win the allegiance of the nobles there and to take what measures he could to protect himself.

"It must be taken through the ahadis," she told Ambar, "to the hand of Prince Shahriyar himself. On thy head be it. If I am held captive, the prince and his wife are also in peril."

The old eunuch pressed the sealed missive to his forehead. "On my life, O Most Imperial. But surely —surely there will be others to take your part."

He managed to get the letter through the guards, and in some fashion to discover what was passing within the lashgar. Late that afternoon he brought his tidings to his lady, who had not slept.

Asaf Khan must have made his plans in advance, because he acted within an hour of Jahangir's death. Farrash and other agents went from group to group of the amirs, suggesting that to avoid civil war a successor be chosen at once. If chosen by the nobles of the lashgar, he would hold them in favor—and the

army of the lashgar was the key to the northern
region. Then Asaf Khan issued a summons to a council, and the amirs, prompted by his envoys, named a
son of Khusrau Padishah—Dawar Bakhsh, a youth
of little decision and no talents. Ceremoniously, he
was led to the Throne, and the great amirs came
before him to swear fealty and perform the *taslim*.

The move disturbed Nur Mahal, cut off as she
was from communication with other leaders. The
officers of the army had followed the example of the
amirs, obeying Asaf Khan. "But why?" she pondered. "There was no need."

"Save to place a descendant of our lord upon the
throne before Prince Shahriyar could arrive, O my
lady," he hazarded.

Still she was not satisfied, and she had pierced to
the core of Asaf's plan before rumors reached her
from the lashgar. Her brother had made a bargain
with the leading amirs. They were to support a tem-
porary occupant of the Throne until Kurram could
arrive with Mahabat Khan from the south. They
three—Kurram and the Sirdar and he—would have
the support of the majority of the nobles, and the
lashgar would unite with the forces of the exiled
prince. They would hold the north with the great
cities of Lahore, Delhi, and Agra, with the imperial
treasures. The Rajput princes would follow Kurram and Mahabat Khan, and the only remaining
imperial army—that of Khan Jahan Lodi, a thousand miles distant—would be unable to stand against
such united power. Meanwhile Nur Mahal was to
be held isolated, and Shahriyar to be seized.

Such was the plan of Asaf Khan, and for the first time Nur Mahal realized that he had shaped events toward this for years, keeping up meanwhile the semblance of friendship for her and devotion to Jahangir.

"Much of this I knew," she thought, "but not that my brother would sacrifice me for Kurram's favor. And what now of Lardili?"

For two days the lashgar marched rapidly south, Nur Mahal a prisoner, bearing Jahangir's body in its winding cloth beside her. When they came out on the plains, she insisted upon the funeral rites being performed and the body laid in a casket. But no one visited her camp.

Asaf Khan had done the one thing possible to undermine the authority of his imperious sister. If she could have spoken with the amirs, she might even then have divided the lashgar and rallied supporters to the cause of Shahriyar. Holding her captive, they felt their fortunes bound to Asaf Khan, who assured them of Kurram's patronage. They dreaded Nur Mahal's anger, yet saw that for the present she could rely upon only one army—that of Shahriyar. Kurram would never make peace with her, or she with Kurram.

As they neared Lahore by rapid stages, Asaf Khan led the armed forces of the imperial lashgar a march ahead of the main body. And the little news that filtered in to Nur Mahal was not reassuring. Shahriyar had done his best to obey her instructions and had given away most of the Lahore treasure to the nobles who professed loyalty to him. No leader him-

self, he had appointed a cousin commander of his
new recruits.

The two armies approached each other rapidly
along the road, with Shahriyar hesitating within
sight of Lahore.

Nur Mahal first knew the result of the battle by
the uproar in the lashgar. Beside her pavilions the
great kettledrums thundered, and the cannon crashed
in salute. Shahriyar had been defeated.

How badly defeated, she learned days later when
the lashgar entered Lahore and she was sent under
guard to rooms in the citadel. The followers of the
prince had broken under the first charges of the
veteran cavalry, and Shahriyar foolishly had shut
himself up in this citadel, while the nobles to whom
he had given immense sums hastened to make their
peace with Asaf Khan. Traitors opened the gates of
the city that same night, and Asaf Khan's columns
rode in triumphantly. No defense of the fort was attempted, and Shahriyar sacrificed the last loyalty of
his people when he took refuge in the harem of his
women—being dragged out to prison by eunuchs.

"If he had been a man!" Nur Mahal said bitterly.

"There remains Khan Jahan," Ambar reminded
her, "who waits like a fox for word from the Most
Imperial."

Erect and silent Nur Mahal looked at the old
negro who had been the confidant of her years of
dominion. He stood before her with his hands crossed
respectfully, hopeful of hearing one of those swift
decisions that had so often solved difficulties in the
past. She was thinking of the long struggle with

Kurram that had sent two armies through the length
of the empire and the battle at the Jhelum when she
had tried to free Jahangir from the power of Mahabat Khan . . . when she had watched the bodies
falling into the river. True, Khan Jahan Lodi had
won over the princes of the Dekkan long since, and
Kurram, she heard, had been forced to make a detour to escape his outposts. But Lardili and Shahriyar were captives—only a desperate war could free
them, and after that, what of India with the Moguls
divided against each other, making a battlefield of
the provinces? . . . She would do nothing more.

So in the end she did make a decision, although not
what Ambar had looked for. "Nay," she said, "it is
finished. I shall send no more commands."

And when he would have protested, she advised
him to leave her, taking Hushiyar and Nazim with
him, as soon as possible. No longer would she have
need of a great household, and presently their enemies would remember the servants who had aided
her plans so often. Asaf Khan would remember, and
Kurram. If they could make her a captive, they
could strangle her servitors.

"Nay," the eunuch's lined face turned to her ap-
pealingly, "I have grown old and fortunate under
thy shadow. I will not leave thee to be served by
others who would make much noise and trouble my
lady, not knowing——"

"Then," she smiled, "will I command thee to go."

It was weeks after the departure of Ambar and the
others that a last appeal was made to Nur Mahal.
From the road Kurram had sent a decree to Asaf

Khan, bidding him send out of the world Dawar Bakhsh, the son of Khusrau and Shahriyar, the brother, with the other surviving grandsons of Akbar. First Kurram's name was read aloud in the mosques of Lahore as Padishah, and then Asaf Khan gave the order for the execution that would remove from Kurram's path the last male descendants of Akbar, other than his own sons.

That evening a nobleman slipped past the guards of the harem, and made himself known to Nur Mahal's maidservants, who hastened to their lady.

"Fedai Khan hath come to the gate and seeks word with the Most Imperial."

Nur Mahal's messenger had come with tidings from men who would support her, after the murder of the princes that day. But the maids returned to the door, and motioned him away.

"Our lady says that this is no more than a house of mourning. She will not lift the veil to speak with men again."

The next day, riding upon one of the imperial elephants, Kurram—now known to all by his reign-title, Shah Jahan—entered the gate of Agra in triumph, his servants tossing gold and silver to the crowds as he made his way to the citadel to take his seat upon the black stone that still bore the reddish stain, as of blood spilled long ago.

The rest is history. Shah Jahan began his reign with all the capacity and the taste for magnificence that had been his as a prince, and with the utterly human devotion to his wife Arjamand that redeemed his natural cruelty. Asaf Khan was richly rewarded, being appointed minister, with the rank of 18,000 horse, and the honorary title of the Right Hand of the State, while the ageing Mahabat Khan became commander in chief with the title of Khan of Khans.

From the day of his accession Shah Jahan did what he could to efface the memory of Nur Mahal. Her property was confiscated, the coins bearing her name gathered into the Mint and taken from circulation. She was allowed a small pension of two lakhs of rupees, and the amount needed to build Jahangir's tomb, which she planned to erect in the Shahdara garden outside Lahore.

Shah Jahan, a most thorough and unforgiving soul, saw to it that the chroniclers of his reign made a record of Nur Mahal's deeds. They admitted that she had fascinated Jahangir, his father, by her beauty, and had dominated him by her ambition. She had, it now appeared, been the heart of the intrigue that made Shah Jahan an outcast as a prince; she had plotted the destruction of that courageous and worthy servant of the State, Mahabat Khan. Her first husband—so the tale was written down—had sought to slay her, to put an end to her fatal beauty when he felt his own death at hand. And she had tried to enmesh Prince Kurram in the snare of her loveliness before he reached the years of discretion. And finally, her ambition would have governed India through the person of Prince Shahriyar, if it had not been for the zeal of that faithful servant of the State, Asaf Khan. So the writers of Shah Jahan made the record of her deeds, falsely.

For a while it was whispered that the Most Imperial had been put to death by order of the Emperor. But that also was false.

We know she lived in retirement for eighteen years, with Lardili—two slender women marked by their grace and seen only when they appeared veiled to walk in the garden under the poplars where Jahangir's tomb now stood complete in its red sandstone and white marble, without a dome—because he had once told her that he wished nothing between his body and the sky. They walked through the cloisters there, giving alms to the beggars who waited at the gate. But they did not lift the heavy mourning veils.

We do not know if she remembered Prithvi's curse, that she should live her last years with empty hands, with the faces of men turned from her. After the death of Jahangir she left no record of her thoughts.

She became a shadow of that many-peopled land, where the rule of the Mogul, for all its outward splendor, was failing, doomed to fall within a century, when the last princes of the house of Genghis Khan would give place to the English from over the sea.

AFTERWORD

THE LEGEND OF NUR MAHAL

ITH time a legend gathered about the name of the Persian who had held India in her hand. This was inevitable. She had come out of the obscurity of the harem, and had retired again into seclusion. She had, it seems, few visitors in those last years, and certainly no chronicler wrote the story of her life from her own viewpoint.

The chroniclers of Shah Jahan's reign were naturally antagonistic to her, and later writers followed them. A woman who had taken the responsibility of the government from one of the Mogul emperors could hope for no leniency from Moslem flatterers of the Moguls. At the same time the brilliancy of her achievement and her personal loveliness could not be denied. Even a cold-blooded Dutch merchant who was in India at the time admits that "she was worshiped as a goddess" until the rebellion of Mahabat Khan. So the legend began to take form, partly to account for an amazing career, partly to extol the characters of Jahangir and Shah Jahan, and partly to explain the magnetism of her own personality.

Nur Mahal became, in this popular tale, a Persian slave gifted with extraordinary beauty and overweening ambition. The circumstance of her birth grew amazingly. Not only was she born in poverty during a caravan journey, but her parents abandoned her by the road, where the infant was guarded by a great snake until the caravan master noticed her and took compassion on her, searching the caravan for a woman to nurse her—that woman being found, naturally enough, in her mother.

Then, upon her marriage to Shir Afgan, the legend related that Jahangir, who had become blindly enamored, pursued her throughout the years. The Mogul sought to slay the soldier, her husband, at first by loosing a tiger—an echo of the incident that gave Shir Afgan his new name—upon him, then by sending a band of armed men against him. In this mythical assassination, Shir Afgan performed wonders, cutting down his enemies until at last he sought to drag himself, dying, back to his home and bury his sword in the body of his beautiful but fatal wife.

The legend continues to explain how Jahangir then summoned her to his court, only to be indignantly repulsed by the proud Persian, who reproached him with the murder of Shir Afgan and refused to enter the imperial harem until, in some way unexplained, he managed to break down her constancy and possess her.

It is a romantic legend, melodramatic enough to

fill a novel. In fact, it has filled the pages of histories until now. From the Persian chronicles of the early eighteenth century, it was taken more or less entire into the pages of the English historians, Dow and Elphinstone, and from these standard works it has migrated into almost every article or story dealing with Nur Mahal. During the writing of this book a two-page article printed in an Indian newspaper, dealing with the marriage of Nur Mahal, was sent to the author. It contained all the legendary incidents.

Scholars of today reject the legend. The daughter of Ghias Beg, instead of being a slave, was well born and highly intelligent. There is no proof that she was abandoned after her birth during the caravan journey. What actually happened was that Malik Masud, the caravan master, became interested in the poverty-ridden Persian family at the time of the birth, and upon their arrival at Fathpur himself presented Ghias Beg to the emperor, Akbar. The astute Persian was given a position in the imperial court, and rose steadily in rank, until Jahangir's marriage to his daughter brought him into high favor. So it is true that the fortunes of Ghias Beg and his son Asaf Khan can be traced to Nur Mahal, even at the beginning.

It is quite certain that Jahangir did not plan the death of Shir Afgan. For one thing, this version of the story was not heard until two generations after. Contemporary chronicles do not speak of it, and European visitors—the Englishmen Hawkins and Sir

Thomas Roe among them—who wrote down much of the court intrigue, which seems to have fascinated them, are silent upon this point. And we cannot believe that Jahangir would have left in his memoirs a circumstantial account of the death of Shir Afgan, if he had planned such a thing. His statement, made within a few days of the event, is clearness itself.

When Shir Afgan (Jahangir relates) heard of the arrival of Kutb ud-Din, who had been sent to arrest him and to punish him for sedition if he proved to be guilty, he went out to meet the governor. When he entered Kutb ud-Din's camp he found himself surrounded by armed men. He exclaimed, "What is going on?" And when Kutb ud-Din motioned back his men and came forward alone, Shir Afgan stabbed him two or three times through the stomach with his sword, also slaying the first man who ran up to him, before being cut down himself.

Two incidents in this book appear in the legend, and are not confirmed. First, the meeting between the girl Mihri and Jahangir in the harem at Fathpur. This, however, is related in detail by Khafi Khan, a chronicler who wrote about a century after the event, and who apparently drew upon material that is now lost.[1]

[1]While gathering material for Nur Mahal, a large portion of Khafi Khan's work, the *Muntakhab-ul-lubab,* dealing with Jahangir and Nur Mahal, was translated for the first time from the Persian under the author's direction at the University of California. The author essayed some slight additional translation from the Persian— the language in which almost all documents of the Mogul period were written originally.

Khafi Khan relates: "The king (Jahangir) wanted her, and the love of her grew in his heart. Until one day he found her alone in the corner of the palace and playfully took her hand, and drew her to him. Nur Mahal went away and complained to the ladies of the palace . . ."

This is not cast in the usual legendary phrasing. And it is extremely probable that Jahangir[1] (then a youthful prince), who had access to the imperial harem, must have seen Mihri there. Scholars admit the likelihood of such a meeting. And it is easier to understand Jahangir's passion for the Persian woman if we concede that they met when Mihri was a girl.

The second point is Mihri's marriage to Shir Afgan, by Akbar's order, to place her beyond Jahangir's reach. Beni Prasad, the latest biographer of Jahangir, does not accept this, saying that Akbar would have had no objection to marrying Jahangir to a woman of Nur Mahal's birth and breeding.

But it is known that Akbar ordered another girl, Anarkali, buried alive on suspicion of being intimate

---

[1] He was then, of course, Prince Salim, and did not acquire the title-name of Jahangir until his accession. But where so many oriental names are involved, as in this book, it is confusing to alter them. So the emperor is called throughout by his most usual name Jahangir, and Prince Kurram is not mentioned as Shah Jahan (his title name) until the end. Mahabat Khan and Asaf Khan appear in their honorary names, while Ghias Beg is barely mentioned as Itimad daula—all these being the usual nomenclature of the histories. While India was then known as Hind to the Persians and Ind or Hindustan to the Moguls themselves, it is mentioned as India in this book. The customary word Moslem is used for *Muslim* and *Musalman*.

NUR MAHAL'S NIGHT RIDES

ORTHODOX MOSLEMS even today do not mention in public the names or affairs of their women. A Turk, for instance, will speak of the good health or the death of his "family." So it is usually the case that the lives of the harem women pass unrecorded. Their names are mentioned in chronicles as the mothers of certain sons, or they are described as the daughters of Such-and-such amirs or princes. In Nur Mahal's case little except hearsay is recorded of her until she began to break through the barrier of seclusion, to take her part in public events. Jahangir, for instance, does not even mention his marriage to her, in his memoirs, while his last pages are full of her doings.

We have also the accounts of contemporary writers such as Mutamad, and the evidence of Sir Thomas Roe, with that of a Dutch scientist, De Laet, who wrote in 1631—all these bearing on the years of her supremacy, roughly from 1616 to 1627.

So the early chapters of this book are pieced together from fragmentary evidence, while the last chapters, following the assassination of Khusrau, are almost entirely fact.

There is no proof that Nur Mahal ventured frequently out of the harem at night, but it is almost certain that she did so. She is known to have been daring, and accustomed to travel in her early years;

313

she could ride well and far—and she did not look upon the law of pardah as the palace-bred Indian wives regarded it. She appeared, veiled of course, in the jharoka window, and talked with the men of the court. Sir Thomas Roe relates that they all had to wait for hours in the audience tent one night, while Nur Mahal took Jahangir for a ride in a bullock cart —she doing the driving. And she accompanied the lashgar everywhere, often riding away on short trips with Jahangir, as in the excursions to the Kangra citadel, and the Kashmir gardens. Finally, when Jahangir was made captive by Mahabat Khan in the surprise attack at the Jhelum, she escaped in disguise with one eunuch, through Mahabat Khan's army, and crossed the river safely. No woman who had spent her years behind the curtain would have been able to do such a thing. The episode of her tiger hunt is fact, by the way. She went on at least one other hunt and killed, according to Jahangir, four tigers with six shots. Considering the crude guns of the period, this feat is almost incredible—but Jahangir is accuracy itself where game is involved.

It is a mistake to assume that the Moslem women of the harem were kept within their rooms. They could go to the mosques and the public baths, or— under proper guard—to visit relatives and make journeys. Moslems are fond of moving about, and in the hot countries, where it is not easy to sleep before midnight, women often ventured out at night with an attendant.

THE POEMS

JAHANGIR was no ordinary drunkard. He was a cultured man, speaking three languages and writing two. He knew a good deal of history and geography, while he became deeply interested in botany and zoölogy. At times his experiments were grotesque, but they were always accurate.

Besides his passion for precious stones, he had a real love for gardens, and his memoirs are filled with pen sketches of flowers in bloom, and miniature lakes. In addition, he was a connoisseur of painting. During his reign and that of Shah Jahan the art of Mogul painting reached its height, while their architects completed some of the best buildings of the Moslem period in India—notably that gem of design, the Taj Mahal.

Even before the conquest of India the Moguls had been intelligent and wayward gentlemen, with a weakness for wine. For nearly a century Jahangir's ancestors had been surrounded by the culture of India, and by the poets and artisans of Persia—the two Eastern countries that had kept alive the flame of Greek culture. Jahangir knew both Plato and Aristotle; he had drawings of Dürer and works of the Italian artists in his collection of paintings.

Naturally his court favored literature—it was a poor amir or cup companion who could not cap a quotation from Hafiz, or improvise a verse. Jahangir's verses limped a little, while Nur Mahal's seemed to be more gifted.

In the Persian chronicle of Khafi Khan some of her verses came to light and were translated into English for this book, probably for the first time. Once Jahangir appeared in a tunic, fastened with a priceless ruby, to which he called her attention. She answered with an improvised couplet:

"That is not a ruby that fastens your vest—
It is a drop of my blood that lies on your breast."

Another couplet of hers is quoted:

"I will not give my heart to thy face,
'Till thy heart is made known to me."

Jahangir's love of good verse is shown by his discovery of the quatrain "of someone" on the pillar of a well, the quatrain that we know as one of the best of Omar Khayyám's.

IT IS so convenient to say of her "Cæsar was ambitious," and having established, as it were, the measure of her character by a phrase, to account for all of her acts without further cogitation. So convenient and so obvious that, following the chroniclers who were her detractors, almost all historians have done so since her death. Beni Prasad, who tells the most intimate story of Jahangir's life, speaks of her "ambitious and dominating temperament," adding that she was "one of those strong intellects who . . . love to dominate every situation, and who tend unconsciously to gather all authority in their hands."

While there is truth in this, it is not all the truth. Nur Mahal was versatile, as only a very few of the great women of the world's courts have been. A hundred years after her death the fashions in dress that she designed were still worn, Khafi Khan relates, except in frontier villages. Her charity to women, of all kinds, is one of the pleasant memories of the Mogul period. Prasad relates that she never heard of an orphan girl without contributing a marriage portion. She dominated the social life of a court which was, perhaps, the most luxurious in the annals of history. And she planned at least two mausoleums—that of her father at Agra, and of Jahangir—which still stand as architectural landmarks of India.

Everything she did is marked by the same intensity
of purpose and high idealism. She aided her father
in his labors as minister and treasurer, and her sorrow at his death is unmistakable. She distrusted her
utterly venal and ambitious brother Asaf Khan, who
struck at her treacherously at least twice—once at
the Jhelum, where he endeavored to betray her with
Jahangir into the hand of Mahabat Khan, and again
the night of Jahangir's death, when he made her a
prisoner. Nur Mahal could have eliminated her
brother by betraying him in turn to Mahabat Khan;
instead she exerted herself to obtain Asaf Khan's
release, after she had freed Jahangir. And it is hard
to believe that she could not have escaped captivity
after Jahangir's death, if she had chosen to plunge
the lashgar into civil strife.

She befriended Kurram, until the murder of
Khusrau, when she turned against him with the same
intensity of feeling; she was the firm ally of Mahabat
Khan until the attack at the Jhelum. And, ambitious,
restless, imperious beyond a doubt, she still re-
nounced all power after the deaths of Jahangir and
Shahriyar, her daughter's husband.

Knowing that, for a certainty, it is interesting to
glance at the verdict of one of the later chroniclers:

A thousand pities that with all this intelligence, after
she had married her daughter that she had by Shir Afgan
to Shahriyar the son of Jahangir, in view of the love that
women have for their daughters' sakes toward their
sons-in-law, and the selfish jealousy they have that makes
a strong man tremble at the thought of it—she fought to

put the guileless Shahriyar ahead, at the expense of the strong crown prince. . . . And without thinking of the future, or the destruction of the throne, or the hurt of the people, she struck the wasp's nest of India into tumult.[1]

Nur Mahal's crime, in the eyes of the chronicler, was in supporting the *guileless* Shahriyar against the *strong* Kurram, who bathed the path to the throne with blood. De Laet, an impartial witness, writes several years after Kurram's accession:

It is easy to foretell that a reign inaugurated by so many crimes will prove to be ill-starred, and a throne buttressed by the shedding of so much innocent blood will prove to be insecure.

In fact, Shah Jahan, eight years before his death, was deposed by his son Aurangzeb, amid intrigue and civil war too well known to need recounting here.

The court dominated by the beauty and wit of Nur Mahal was as sophisticated and intrigue-ridden as the Rome of the Cæsars or the France of the later Valois; but even her enemies among the chroniclers do not accuse Nur Mahal of eliminating any of her antagonists by poison or assassination—a commonplace in the careers of Cleopatra and Catherine de' Medici. And no one has ever questioned her devotion to Jahangir.

What she felt for the debauched emperor—whether she returned his passionate love, or gave to him

[1] Translated from the Persian of Khafi Khan.

the same instinct of protection that shielded her daughter—we do not know. It is one of her many secrets.

Jahangir was no man's fool; he could be led but not driven. Until the advent of Nur Mahal no one person dominated him, nor could she have done so through his physical passion alone. Jahangir found in her a woman of surpassing loveliness, who studied his temperament, spared him the exertion of governing, and ministered to his craving for diversion. Until his physical breakdown became complete, she did not assume, outwardly, the entire responsibility of government.

She was a woman, struggling—if you wish—for an ideal, or more probably actuated by a purely human desire to live her own life in a world of men. Until the last she would not yield in the least to any of them. Her political power was overthrown by that final triumvirate, the brilliant Kurram, the audacious Mahabat Khan, and the treacherous Asaf Khan; but all three were common clay compared to Nur Mahal.

Perhaps a European of her century has said the most truthful thing about her:

When we scrutinize her actions we find in them no fault, save that she was a woman.

SELDOM does a writer approach a character from as many angles as in the case of Nur Mahal. There is, of course, no biography of the Mogul empress—the present writer knows of no volume devoted to her, or any full account of her. Even anecdotes, except for the popular legend mentioned earlier, are lacking. There are only paragraphs in histories, and short sketches in general works dealing with India.

Some years ago I formed the idea of trying to reconstruct Nur Mahal's life from contemporary evidence. Since then I have worked at it from time to time, gradually accumulating the witnesses within the shelves of my library. They are all before me now, in the worn brown leather of three centuries ago, for the most part, with some orthodox blue backs of the Royal Asiatic Society, a few imposing tomes of the Bibliotheca Indica—kindly loaned by the Cornell University Library—with Khafi Khan in manuscript translation. Buried within them are fragments of the life that was Nur Mahal's.[1]

[1] The titles mentioned below are not given as a bibliography for the study of Nur Mahal and her period—a study which embraces a variety of subjects, ranging from the Mongol traditions and the religion of Islam to such details as saddlery and wines. The present writer has found the titles given here to be most important as well as most interesting to anyone desiring information about Nur Mahal, Jahangir, or the court of the Moguls.

The Setting

My first effort was to identify the Mogul court, with its people as it existed when she entered it.

For this purpose Abu'l Fazl proved to be a priceless guide. He was Akbar's minister, assassinated by Jahangir, and he left a description of the government in all its details, with plans of the imperial lashgar—his work being entitled the *Ain-i-Akbari,* translated by Blochmann from Persian into English. The editor, fortunately for a searcher, added biographical notes of all Akbar's family and the nobles of the court.

Next came a different aspect, the rollicking memoirs of Jahangir's grandfather, Babar—a masterpiece in its own right, reciting the adventures of the conqueror of India down to the year 1527. With this I read the *Humayun Nama,* which is the Story of Humayun, by Gul Badan Begam—Princess Rosebody, one of Babar's daughters, who wrote a colorful little narrative of the women's world which shared the wanderings of Humayun, Padishah of India and Babar's son. In this are discovered many of the women's troubles and festivals, and those two Tartar princesses Salima and Ruqaiya.

Witnesses of the Time

The chief witness should have been Jahangir. But his memoirs do not mention his wife frequently until the last five years—it is extraordinary in a Moslem prince to speak of her at all. None the less, the *Tuzuk-i-Jahangiri,* gives an inimitable glimpse of the emperor's mind and temper. Several scenes in this book, such as the first tiger hunt, are practically rewritten from the memoirs.

The second witness is Mutamad, the scribe and paymaster of the emperor. His work, titled the *Ikbalnama,* gives a rough chronicle of the reign, with a disapproving notice of Nur Mahal. To the *Ikbalnama* are added other anecdotes by Persian writers of the day—including a valuable note by a servant describing Jahangir's daily routine, with a summary of Mahabat Khan's letter of protest against Nur Mahal.

Among the European witnesses, my particular favorite is Sig. Pietro della Valle, a noble Roman and adventurous soul who journeyed to the East as an alternative to suicide, and joined in the wars of Turkey and Persia, marrying twice en route and having fourteen sons by his second wife, a Georgian.

The most important, of course, is worthy Sir Thomas Roe, whose journal under the title *Embassy of Sir Thomas Roe to the Great Mogul* has become a classic. The good ambassador—the first to go from England to India—gives a detailed account of the court, the lashgar, his own dealings with Jahangir, and a fine character sketch of Prince Kurram.

The next impartial witness is a Dutchman, but more of a scholar. I found De Laet's *Empire of the Great Mogol* valuable for its description of the palaces at Agra, and the events of Jahangir's reign. Pelsaert, another Dutchman, gives in his *Remon-*

strantie a rather dry account of India's trade, with a sudden and surprisingly vivid picture of harem life, which has gone into this book.

Jesuits add their word. The *Relations* of Father Guerreiro give an account of Jahangir and his conversations with the Christian priests.

The next witness is the blunt English sea dog William Hawkins who was in India from 1607 to 1612, matching cups and jests with Jahangir, and giving on the whole a clear account of the court ceremonies, mingled with weird tales of what he heard.

Reverend Edward Terry, appointed chaplain to Sir Thomas Roe, left in his *Voyage to East India* a full account of all he observed in the empire, with a description of the plague and the lashgar on the march.

All these seven Europeans are alike—they give only gossip concerning Nur Mahal (Hawkins left before her marriage to the emperor). But this contemporary gossip is interesting, and sometimes true.

The Next Reign

The work of Khafi Khan—*Muntakhab ul lubab*—in Persian was translated in part for this book. I found that the chronicler repeated much of the legend of Nur Mahal, besides information not found elsewhere and obviously true.

The European travelers have grown more discriminating. Peter Mundy, a factor of the East India Company, gives some interesting accounts of the towns as they were in Aurangzeb's day. François

Bernier, a French physician, wrote one of the best travel books of all time in his *Voyages,* colorful accounts of city life in India, the lashgar, and the Kashmir resorts.

Monsieur de Thevenot possessed an extraordinary mind. He traveled through the Near East to India and wrote down detailed descriptions of every serai and local custom on the way. His volume—a huge one in old leather—supplies an almost perfect stage setting for the seventeenth century. Niccolao Manucci, an Italian physician, in his *Storio di Mogor,* gives some interesting experiences in doctoring women of the harem, but his gossip is not to be trusted.

Three modern historians are important. James Tod, in his famous *Annals and Antiquities of Rajast'han,* supplies all the data a man could wish upon the Rajputs. Vincent Smith's life of Akbar is the best biography of that monarch. Beni Prasad's *History of Jahangir* is the only trustworthy biography of the emperor, and has proved most useful to this writer.

THE END